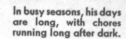

Records prove each horse costs more than 13 cents every hour to operate.

Days behind a team are long, full of hard work . . . yet less work is done.

Dusk finds him still working, for the next day it may rain and stop work.

When he finally comes in, he must unharness, feed, bed, curry the horses.

In busy seasons, his days are long, with chores running long after dark.

Horses and extra help to cultivate . . . his power isn't built to do all jobs.

Late afternoon, work yet to do . . . he wishes he had time to feed some cattle.

Handling the heavy tractor has been hard work; he comes in tired and sore.

Before he can clean up and sit down to eat his supper, darkness has fallen.

Evenings are short; long days make him too tired to enjoy them.

Big tires, fenders, comfortable seat, easy steering make his work easier.

The job done sooner, he has time to develop more money-making activities.

His tractor has brought him more spare time, to sit back and enjoy life.

He has freed himself from dawn-to-dark drudgery, won greater independence.

He has time to plan his farming so that his land will pay bigger profits.

You Rather Spend?

man with a slow, cumbersome tractor who has trouble getting his work done on time and who must keep horses to do some of his work because he does not have power that does every job. Fast, versatile power, such as you get in the "WC" tractor, helps you farm better and make more money, bringing freedom from the toil that chains you to your land. It brings you freedom from dawn-to-dark drudgery, and gives you . . . daylight farming.

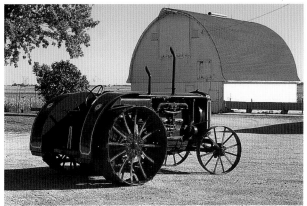

"This book is about Allis Chalmers tractors. . . . It's about farmers for whom an old Allis represented an enormous leap into the future, a machine that was—and is—a miracle of engineering, a faithful friend, and an economic blessing."
—Roger Welsch

Vintage Allis-Chalmers Tractors

The Ultimate Tribute to
Allis-Chalmers Tractors

Foreword by Roger Welsch
Text by Lynn K. Grooms
Photography by Chester Peterson Jr.
With a chapter on Allis-Chalmers in Europe by Bill Huxley

Japonica Press

Edited by Michael Dregni
Designed by Andrea Rud
Cover design by Paul Banks
Front cover photograph by Peter D. Simpson
Printed in Hong Kong

ISBN 0-9533737-7-0

A catalogue record for this book is available from the British Library.

First published in the United Kingdom in 2000 by
Japonica Press
Low Green Farm
Hutton
Driffield
East Yorkshire
YO25 9PX

First published in the United States in 2000 by Voyageur Press, Inc., Stillwater, MN 55082 U.S.A.

Legal Notice
This is not an official publication of AGCO/Allis-Chalmers or Fiat. The name Allis-Chalmers, as well as certain names, model designations, and logo designs, are the property of AGCO. We use them for identification purposes only. Neither the author, photographer, publisher, nor this book are in any way affiliated with AGCO, Allis-Chalmers, or Fiat.

Charles Freitag's painting is reproduced by permission of the artist and Apple Creek Publishing, 101 Fisher Street, Hiawatha, IA 52233.

ON THE ENDPAPERS: *Comparison of farming methods from a 1940s Allis-Chalmers WV brochure.*

ON THE FRONTISPIECE: *A farm boy sits astraddle his favorite tractor. (Library of Congress) A 1920s Model L 12/20. The dynamic duo: 1983 4W220, left, and 1985 4W305.*

ON THE TITLE PAGES: *"Grandpa's Farm," an oil painting by Iowa artist Charles Freitag. (Apple Creek Publishing)*
INSET ON THE TITLE PAGE: *"Relax and Enjoy your Power Farming" brochure from Allis-Chalmers.*

ON THE CONTENTS PAGE: *A 1940 Model B on steel wheels due to the rubber shortage during World War II.*

Acknowledgments

*A*lthough you only see the bylines on this book's cover, an effort such as this is really the result of the assistance and cooperation of a number of people.

We'd like to give special, heartfelt thanks to restorers and/or tractor owners—not to mention great people—Donald Fanetti, Mike Gathje, Lavern Greif, Robert Janecek, Edwin and Larry Karg, Kent Kaster, Ron Knarr, Kris and Loretta Leable, John Nelson, Mark and Dave Pfouts, Steve and Rachel Rosenboom, and Herschel L. Surratt.

We'd also like to thank Norm Swinford and John Allen for their help in obtaining black-and-white archival photographs; Dr. Ron Schuler, Department Chairman, Agricultural Engineering, University of Wisconsin–Madison, for pointing us in the right direction for Allis-Chalmers research; and the Wisconsin Historical Society for use of its valuable resources.

Finally, a thanks to Bill Huxley for his history of Allis-Chalmers in Great Britain and Europe.

Dedication

*T*hey're out in their shops on many a cold and snowy winter evening, and on more than a few of the year's weekends, too. They disassemble, they scrape, they scrounge for parts, they nurse bloody knuckles, they reassemble in like-new or better condition, they paint, and they attach authentic decals. Then their big moment comes. Fuel, air, and spark are all that are needed for combustion. But, will these cold, unfeeling hunks of metal on which so much time and effort have been lavished actually turn over, and start? Hooray! They purr and growl just like they did when they first rolled off the assembly lines so many years before. Success.

Now to start looking around for the next challenges, the next candidates for careful, loving restorations. . . .

We salute the many restorers of all lines of farm equipment, the people who are ensuring that a vital part of our agricultural heritage is preserved for those who come after.

Contents

FOREWORD

Sweet Allis

By Roger Welsch

*R*oger Welsch's writings on tractors appear regularly in *Successful Farming* magazine's "Ageless Iron" section, as well as in *Esquire*, *Smithsonian*, and *Nebraska Farmer* magazines. In addition, he is the author of more than twenty books, including *Old Tractors and the Men Who Love Them* and *Busted Tractors and Rusty Knuckles*, and is a contributor to *This Old Farm* and *This Old Tractor*, published by Voyageur Press.

MAIN PHOTO: **Roger Welsch, Allis-Chalmers fan**
Noted humorist, author, and speaker Roger Welsch of Dannebrog, Nebraska, is almost as well known for his love of Allis-Chalmers tractors as for his zest for a funny line.

INSET: **1938 Model WC**
The WC was one of the most economical tractors Allis-Chalmers ever produced—and even today it is beloved by Allis fans.

ALLIS·CHALMERS
TRACTOR DIVISION—MILWAUKEE, U.S.A.

Twenty years ago I married a Czech girl from one of the most heavily Czech areas of Nebraska, Butler County. Czechs are wonderful people—full of fun and goodwill, hardworking, honest, generous—so I was delighted to become a part of this extended family and new community. I suppose I should have known, but nonetheless I was surprised when shortly after Linda and I were married, I discovered I was not just welcome among my new family, I had become a real and express part of it. For them, the phrase "son-in-law" was not a formality, it was *reality*, and my new status came along, as diplomas like to have it, with "all the rights and privileges appertaining thereto."

That would have been a blessing enough, but it wasn't all. Not long after that first realization, I had another: I was not only being accepted as a member of my new family and community, I had come to think of myself as a member of the family and community. Somehow, by cultural osmosis, I had become not only a Hotovy, but a Czech. Even *jaternice* and *kolaches* seemed to taste better—and they had been delicious even when I was still a German!

Okay, it may be a bit of an exaggeration, but not much, to say that much the same thing happened to me in my relationship with Allis-Chalmers tractors. (But maybe we should just keep that between us and not share it with Linda and her family!) I would have loved Linda even if she had been Irish, Hispanic, or, gulp, German, of course, but that she is Czech has substantially altered my own perception of myself.

Same with Allises. That day twenty years ago when Dave Ratliff, an old buddy, remarked in an off-handed way, "Rog, if you're going to call this place a farm, you really need a tractor. I have one I haven't used a couple years, sitting and rusting in a backwoods weed patch about 150 miles from here. If you want it, you can have it." He could have been talking about a John Deere, Minneapolis-Moline, or Kubota. I wouldn't have known or cared. I'd never sat on a tractor seat in my life. I didn't even know what I would do with a tractor, or what a 1938 Allis-Chalmers WC might look like, any more than twenty years ago I could have imagined what kind of twenty-five-year-old Catholic Czech girl I could possibly fall in love with.

But in both cases, it seemed like a good idea. And as it turned out, in both cases, it was. Just as surely as I fell in love with Lovely Linda, I fell in love with Sweet Allis. (But

1930s Allis-Chalmers crawlers
A quartet of hefty Allis-Chalmers crawler tractors. From left, a 1937 Model M, 1937 Model MO, 1930 Model U with a Trackson crawler conversion, and 1937 Model WK.

10

again, maybe this is information we best keep among ourselves and not bother Linda with, okay?!) I had no intentions of doing it, but there it was, and once it happened, there was no way to back out.

Sweet Allis served me well for years, always starting, even after sitting in the rain, snow, cold, and wind for months without being started, even when no other internal-combustion engines on the place would start. Folks in town soon learned her name and waved even more vigorously when I drove her into town. And when I didn't drive Sweet Allis, they asked why. Sweet Allis had become an inexorable part of me, and I of her. Neither of us was entirely complete without the other.

For the first time in my life, I had become genuinely fond of a piece of iron. For the first time in my life, I didn't just start an engine and go. Now I twisted a crank, listened with joy to the sound of an engine, rode with pride, really worried about the welfare of a motor vehicle. And remember, this is not a pretty tractor to begin with. It was not a restored prize, or treasure, or rarity. It was—is—just an old tractor.

Which is not to say that I did well by her. I have taught my daughter Antonia to recite on command the mantra, "All men are pigs," and nowhere was that more true than in my . . . uh . . . relationship with Sweet Allis. I had never changed the oil in an automobile in the almost fifty years of my life; I took my cars to a service station and said, "Do whatever it is you do," and they did it. I did that a couple times with Sweet Allis, but I learned early on that you just don't take a tractor to a mechanic for service. It just isn't done. As a result, Sweet Allis survived pretty much on her own momentum, with not even the most basic maintenance.

And yet despite being ignored and abused, she started for me every

This book is about Allis-Chalmers tractors. It's about changes in American history, a transformation of the rude and unlettered peasant hoping to grow enough to keep his family alive to the sophisticated cyber-technician who feeds the world.
—Roger Welsch

1949 Model G
The G was ideal for use as a garden tractor or on truck farms. In fact, it's still a highly sought-after tractor for such work.

time, did whatever was asked of her, stood in the hot sun at the curb while I went into Eric's for a cold one. And then started again and took me home.

It was only many years later that I for some reason got another Allis WC, this time a 1938 model. And then, again utterly mysteriously, for some reason I decided to change the oil in this new acquisition myself. And then maybe fix a broken hand brake. And then, before I knew it, I was swept into a maelstrom from which I would never swim my way out, a terminal case of love for antique tractors and mechanicking, for rust and wrenches, stuck pistons and shattered bearings, and all the things I have come to love and that have provoked Linda again and again to ask, "And *this* is what you call fun?"

And into a love affair for Allis-Chalmers WCs. It's not that I think for a moment they are more valuable, or useful, or pretty, or interesting, or powerful, or fast than, say, Linda's John Deere B. Or my Farmall Cub. It's just that we have become an "item," Sweet Allis and I, and I'm too flattered by the association to fight the inevitable.

Just as my affection for Linda and her family swept me into an entire community and new ethnic identity, my attraction to Allis-Chalmers WC serial number 67,667—a.k.a. Sweet Allis—has led me to an affinity for another three dozen unstyled WCs, and then some styled models of the same tractor, and then to a broader identity with anything Persian orange—a G, two Cs, a couple WDs, a CA—and ultimately to old tractors in general.

And perhaps more remarkably to a whole new circle of non-metallic friends—other collectors, restorers, and admirers of old iron. So, in a matter of a couple years, here's this old English professor, not just non-mechanical but dang near anti-mechanical twenty years ago, sitting around with a lot of other people—I was going to say "old guys," but a lot of them aren't that old these days, and some of them are way too pretty to be called "guys"—talking tools and parts, problems and joys, bargains and booboos, and tractors, tractors, tractors.

This book is about Allis-Chalmers tractors, but you know, it really isn't about Allis-Chalmers tractors. It's about a lot more than that. It's about farmers for whom an old Allis represented an enormous leap into the future, a machine that was—and is—a miracle of engineering, a faithful friend, and an economic blessing. It's about changes in American history, a transformation of the rude and unlettered peasant hoping to grow enough to keep his family alive to the sophisticated cyber-technician who feeds the world. The story of Allis-Chalmers is an incredibly important part of the modern world, and yet it is a chapter seldom read—mostly because it is a chapter that has been rarely written.

That's what I tell Linda. I'm not sure I'd be comfortable telling her how I really feel—pretty much the way I feel about a good pair of old boots or overalls, or a fine dog, or a prized tool. There's something special about those kinds of things, and about my Allises, and it's not easy to explain to someone who isn't in on the secret. I suppose you could call it love, but I'm not sure grown and fairly well educated men are supposed to confess to having affairs with pieces of machinery.

If you're reading this book, and you've read this far, well then, you probably understand about Sweet Allis and me. Of course you can never understand that completely, because even I don't understand what happened between us, me and that Persian orange sweetie of mine. Maybe you've even had something of that feeling along the way yourself.

The story of Allis-Chalmers is an incredibly important part of the modern world, and yet it is a chapter seldom read—mostly because it is a chapter that has been rarely written.
—Roger Welsch

Allis Chalmers Company's Plant, ~~Waukesha, Wis.~~
Milwaukee, Wis.

CHAPTER 1

The Roots of Allis-Chalmers

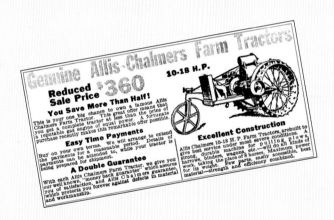

MAIN PHOTO: **Allis-Chalmers factory**
A postcard view of the Allis-Chalmers works in Milwaukee, Wisconsin, from the 1910s. With smoke pouring from the numerous stacks and trains delivering raw materials and hauling away new products, the factory was obviously hard at work building tractors and other farm implements.

INSET: **1923 Model 10/18 advertisement**

ALLIS-FARM CHALMERS-TRACTORS

The history of Allis-Chalmers is as rich as the Persian orange paint that graced its farm tractors for nearly six decades. The company's roots stretch back to 1847, when Charles Decker and James Seville began manufacturing French burr millstones and grist- and flour-mill supplies in Milwaukee, Wisconsin. A few years later, Decker & Seville's Reliance Works expanded into water wheels, shafting and gearing equipment, and other products.

Decker & Seville's Reliance Works rolled along until the late 1850s when it ran into financial difficulties during the economic depression preceding the American Civil War. The financial Panic of 1857 and increasing debt soon forced Reliance Works into bankruptcy.

The bankrupt company was acquired in a sheriff's sale on May 11, 1861, by the brokerage and accounting firm of C. D. Nash, John P. McGregor, and Edward Phelps Allis. In the pre–Civil War depression, this firm reportedly lent Decker & Seville $2,000. Reliance Works was valued at $6,000, and the brokers reportedly purchased the company for a mere $22.72.

Within two weeks of the sheriff's sale, Allis became the sole owner of Reliance Works. The newly christened Edward P. Allis & Company advertised its products for the first time on May 25, 1861, in the Milwaukee *Sentinel* newspaper. Allis also moved the old plant to a new location on Milwaukee's south side, at Clinton and Florida Streets. The Decker & Seville works were split up into three parts and floated section by section on barges down the Milwaukee River to the south-side location where the factory was re-assembled into a crude likeness of its former self.

Allis was born in Cazenovia, New York, in 1824, the son of Jere and Mary Allis. He earned a law degree from Union College in Schenectady, New York. Allis later moved from New York to Wisconsin to go into the leather business with William Allen, a former college classmate. Their Empire Leather Store opened in 1846, but Allis sold his interest in the company in 1856, just prior to the Panic of 1857.

Allis and Allen also operated the Mammoth Tanneries in Two Rivers, Wisconsin. As a supplier of leather goods of all types, Allis had often done business with Decker & Seville. In addition to being a partner in the brokerage firm, Allis was a trustee of the Merchants Mutual Insurance Company and was on the board of directors of the Milwaukee Board of Trade, Fox River Valley Railroad, Northern Illinois Railroad Company, and later, the Milwaukee Chamber of Commerce.

By 1869, Edward P. Allis & Company was manufacturing flour and lumber mills, related equipment and supplies, gearing and shafting equipment, and general ironwork. Between 1869 and 1889, the company expanded foundry capacity by acquiring the Bay State Iron Works of Milwaukee and hiring more engineers to expand the company's product line. By 1870, the firm employed 200 people, and its business volume had increased from $31,000 in 1861 to $350,000.

In the late 1800s, Allis bid to supply piping and pumping machinery to Milwaukee's new waterworks. The firm had not produced pipes up to this time, but even so, Allis won the contract, which called for the manu-

facture of 2,600 tons (2,340 metric tons) of pipe. Once the pipes were completed, the company hired R. W. Hamilton of the Corliss Engine Works of Hartford, Connecticut, to design the pumping engines. In September 1874, Milwaukee's new water plant was put to work. The contract had called for a pumping capability of 16 million gallons (60.8 million liters) every twenty-four hours, but the Allis engines were said to have easily pumped 20 million (76 million liters). Allis's long career of supplying pumping equipment had begun.

ALLIS STEAM POWER

Edward Allis was a forward-thinking entrepreneur. In the mid-1800s, he predicted the importance steam power would play in the lives of people and industry. In 1869, Allis & Company produced its first steam engine.

Allis had set out to become the industry leader in steam power. Since the Corliss steam engine from the Corliss Engine Works was considered the leading engine of the day, Allis persuaded Corliss Chief Engineer Edwin Reynolds to leave that firm and join Allis in 1877.

In 1878, Allis introduced the Reynolds-Corliss engine. This steam engine was so fuel efficient that the company offered to replace any throttle-valve engine in any mill with its Reynolds-Corliss unit. Moreover, Allis agreed to accept payment only for what the engine saved in fuel in 300 to 500 days. This was an offer mill owners could not refuse—but those who studied the phenomenal savings soon realized it was less expensive to pay for the engine itself.

Reynolds also made history with his development of the first direct-acting metallic-valve blowing engine in 1880, which soon became the industry standard. In 1886, Reynolds and his nephew, Irving, designed

1914–1916 Rotary Plow
Soon after Allis-Chalmers ventured into the farm-equipment business in 1913, it licensed American production of the Motoculture Motor-Driven Rotary Plow from Motoculture Ltd. of Switzerland. Allis engineers modified the machine's design, but apparently farmers were not attracted to the tiller as few were built or sold. (Courtesy Norm Swinford)

the first triple-expansion pumping engine for a Milwaukee pumping station. Allis reported that tests showed the highest efficiencies ever attained by a pumping engine. Soon, the firm was shipping these engines to cities around the Midwest. By 1882, the company reported annual revenues of $3 million.

In 1888, Reynolds designed the first screw pump. This pump moved 500 million gallons (1.9 billion liters) of water per day, and was the forerunner of the propeller-type hydraulic turbine.

Allis's firm was also farsighted in employee relations. In 1883, the company's employees joined a health and accident insurance plan, in which the company offered to match funds contributed by employees. The firm created this insurance match before laws required employers to pay compensation for work-related injuries.

By 1900, Edward P. Allis & Company was known worldwide, and the firm received orders from around the globe for Reynolds-Corliss engines to drive electric-power generators. The company was also the world's largest producer of engines for electric street railways and electric light plants.

When Edward P. Allis died in April 1889, his wife, three sons—William W., Edward P. Jr., and Charles—and chief engineer Reynolds assumed the company's management. Like Allis, Reynolds was forward thinking, and envisioned the firm's expansion into more and larger engines and machines.

THE CREATION OF ALLIS-CHALMERS

In 1900, Reynolds attended a meeting of the National Metal Trade Association and happened to discuss his ideas about producing larger machines for the world market with W. J. Chalmers, president of Fraser & Chalmers Company of Chicago, Illinois. Their conversation eventually led to the merger that formed the Allis-Chalmers Company in May 1901. This merger also included Gates Iron Works of Chicago and Dickson Manufacturing Company of Scranton, Pennsylvania.

Fraser & Chalmers brought to the merger its mining machinery line, which supplied mines around the world. Gates Iron Works brought its gyratory crusher and cement-making machinery to the table, whereas Dickson brought compressors, engine tanks, and locomotives.

The officers of the newly incorporated Allis-Chalmers included Charles Allis as president, William Allis as chairman of the board, Edwin Reynolds as chief engineer, and W. J. Chalmers as executive committee chairman.

We know that the tractor is an economic necessity.
—Allis-Chalmers ad credo, 1920s

1915–1916 Tractor Truck
Allis-Chalmers engineers developed a prototype of the half-track Tractor Truck in 1915. Few of the machines were sold, however. Potential customers may have been scared off by the $5,000 price tag. (Courtesy Norm Swinford)

The directors' plans to expand the company's production necessitated building a new plant, which Reynolds designed. They agreed upon buying the 100-acre (40-hectare) Whitemore farm west of Milwaukee for $25,000. Almost overnight, the unsettled vicinity about the farm came to life. Realty companies sprang up to furnish prospective employees of the new industrial center with homes. On March 28, 1902, the new village was named West Allis.

Allis-Chalmers grew significantly as a result of the merger and the new product lines. By 1910, the company employed some 10,000 people and produced $20 to $30 million worth of machinery each year.

1914 Bull advertisement
The Minneapolis, Minnesota, maker of the innovative Bull tractor offered to jointly build the machine with Allis-Chalmers. General Otto Falk declined, and Allis instead copied aspects of the Bull in creating its first true tractor, the Model 10/18. The Bull later laid the foundation for today's Toro Manufacturing Company.

MOVING INTO THE FARM-EQUIPMENT BUSINESS

Such intense expansion and diversification soon resulted in financial difficulties for the fledgling firm. By New Year's Eve 1912, bankruptcy loomed. As a result, General Otto H. Falk and Delmar W. Call were named as the company's receivers on April 8, 1912.

Falk was a Wisconsin National Guard brigadier general. He had attended a local academy, as well as the Allen Military College in Chicago, where he graduated with the rank of captain. In 1886, he was made adjutant general. He was a volunteer in the Spanish American War, later becoming chief engineer of the general staff in Wisconsin. He retired as brigadier general in 1911. Falk also operated his own Falk Company of Milwaukee, a machinery-manufacturing firm.

On April 16, 1913, Falk's newly organized Allis-Chalmers Manufacturing Company was incorporated under the laws of Delaware. Falk and his colleagues worked to coordinate equipment, facilities, and personnel between the group of merged companies. By 1915, the company was out of the red. The next year, it showed a $3 million profit on sales of more than $19 million.

1914 Model 10/18 prototype
The lightweight Bull tractor influenced many pioneering tractor designs, including Allis's prototype 10/18. Production of the kerosene-fueled 10/18 began in 1915. (Courtesy Norm Swinford)

Falk was the driving force behind Allis-Chalmers's entry into the farm-equipment business. He believed the company needed to balance its focus on heavy industry with developing equipment for a new industry that was just beginning to take off. At the forefront of this new industry at the dawn of the twentieth century was the internal-combustion engine, which would soon become a driving force behind an agricultural revolution.

Allis-Chalmers also was attuned to the development of the gasoline traction engine. The first gas traction engines were huge, cumbersome, and difficult to operate. Even so, eleven companies were making them by 1906. Falk foresaw how changing farm demographics could boost farm-equipment manufacturers. A scarcity of farm labor indicated to the General the need for greater mechanization, and indeed, between 1910 and 1914, the number of tractors used on farms would grow by an astounding 170 percent.

1910s Model 10/18
The 10/18 was Allis's first attempt at manufacturing a tractor. This mid-1910s 10/18 bears serial number 1273. It's the oldest Allis tractor known to exist. (Courtesy Mark and Dave Pfouts)

1918 Model 10/18 advertisement
"Here is a tractor that is built right and backed right—a machine that represents the finished work of the best designers and largest engine builders in America," states this early ad.

EARLY TRACTOR PROJECTS

Allis-Chalmers ventured into the farm-equipment business in 1913, when it licensed American production of the Motoculture Motor-Driven Rotary Plow from Motoculture Ltd. of Switzerland. Allis-Chalmers modified the tiller's design, but farmers apparently were not attracted to the plow. Offered from 1914 through 1916, few of them were built and sold.

About the same time, Allis-Chalmers engineers began work on a Tractor Truck. By 1915, the company had developed a prototype, which went into limited production until 1916. Again, few of the Tractor Trucks were sold, perhaps because farmers balked at the accompanying $5,000 price tag.

General Falk was offered the opportunity to enter into a joint venture with the Bull Tractor Company of Minneapolis, Minnesota, to build its heralded Bull tractor. Falk declined the deal, however, and Allis-Chalmers began work on its own first true tractor, the Model 10/18.

1914–1921 MODEL 10/18

Taking design ideas from the Bull tractor, Allis-Chalmers engineers finished a Model 10/18 prototype in 1914, and production of the 4,800-pound (2,160-kg) tractor began in 1915. The tractor featured a one-piece, heat-treated steel frame. It sold for $1,950, and could plow twenty acres (8 hectares) per day on about fifteen gallons (57 liters) of gas.

The tractor was powered by an Allis-Chalmers horizontally opposed two-cylinder engine that started on gasoline and then switched to kerosene after the engine was warm. With a 5.25x7.00-inch (131.25x175-mm) bore and stroke, the engine displaced 303 ci (4,963 cc). As the model number indicated, the tractor's drawbar power was 10 hp and belt power was 18 hp, a common way of rating tractors in those days. The Model 10/18 was never evaluated in the University of Nebraska Tractor Tests as only a few of these machines were made after the Tractor Test Bill became law in July 1919.

The Model 10/18 had a single forward and single reverse speed of 2.33 mph (3.7 kmh). It also had a Detroit force-feed lubricator, Kingston double carburetor, and high-tension magneto.

Allis-Chalmers's first tractor boasted three wheels—two 56-inch (140-cm) rear drive wheels and a single front wheel offset to the right of the machine. The offset front wheel was not easy to steer when operating under heavy drawbar load and so the Model 10/18 was not as popular with farmers as it might have been. The company would rectify this just a few years later when it created a four-wheel tractor.

1910s Moline Universal advertisement

Allis copied the design of the eccentric Universal tractor from the Universal Tractor Company of Columbus, Ohio, which was later acquired by the Moline Plow Company of Moline, Illinois. Moline filed suit against Allis, and Allis was forced to pay royalties to the Moline firm.

1919–1926 GENERAL PURPOSE MODEL 6/12, MODEL B, AND DUPLEX

In 1915, Allis-Chalmers began developing the Model 6/12. Built for general farm use, the 6/12 had two steel front driving wheels that were pivoted by a central turning mechanism. The operator sat at the end of a long pole mounted atop two smaller and lighter wheels at the rear.

The 6/12 was a design copy of the innovative Universal tractor produced by the Universal Tractor Company of Columbus, Ohio, starting in 1913 and was later bought out by the Moline Plow Company of Moline, Illinois, in 1915. Moline later filed patent infringement charges against Allis-Chalmers concerning the 6/12, and Allis-Chalmers was forced to

1919 Model 6/12

Built for general farm use, the Model 6/12 was smaller and lighter than the 10/18. It had two steel driving wheels in the front pivoted by a central turning mechanism. The tractor operator sat at the end of the long pole on lighter wheels at the rear. This 6/12 was mounted with an Oliver plow from the famed Oliver Chilled Plow Company of South Bend, Indiana. (Courtesy Norm Swinford)

pay royalties to the Moline firm.

The gasoline-powered tractor featured a four-cylinder LeRoi engine of 3.12x4.50-inch (78x112.50-mm) bore and stroke, displacing 138 ci (2,260 cc) and rated at 1,200 rpm. Drive was via a single forward gear propelling the tractor up to 2.5 mph (4 kmh). The Nebraska Tests measured 6.29 drawbar and 12.37 belt hp with a 1,046-pound (470-kg) pull. The tractor weighed just 2,500 pounds (1,125 kg).

During the time the 6/12 was made, Allis-Chalmers built a tractor a day on average. The 6/12 retailed for $850. The company made 700 of these tractors, but demand was less than expected and about 200 were sold at prices as low as $295.

RIGHT: **1920s Model 6/12**
This 6/12 pulls a one-bottom 16-inch (40-cm) Oliver plow.

BELOW: **1920s Model 6/12**
The Model 6/12 was created to replace draft horses on small farms. The 6/12 could use a farmer's existing horse-drawn implements. Any implement with a tongue could be mounted, thanks to the tractor's articulating front end. (Courtesy Dave Pfouts and John Nelson)

Allis-Chalmers built a Model B version of the 6/12 with the engine mounted lower in the frame, making it ideal for orchard use. In addition, 6/12 Cane and 6/12 Industrial versions were offered in small numbers in the early 1920s.

With the 6/12, Allis-Chalmers made history in 1919 by offering its Duplex version that combined two 6/12 tractors mounted back to back. The Duplex was the brainchild of Chief Consulting Engineer Johann F. "Max" Patitz and offered farmers a pioneering tandem tractor for heavy-duty work. As Patitz wrote in an Allis-Chalmers brochure of the day, "The Allis-Chalmers Duplex is formed by joining two 6–12s together into one unit. The transmission controls of the two tractors are interlocked so that they operate as one. . . . This Allis-Chalmers Duplex Tractor with four driving wheels will pull three 16-inch [40-cm] bottoms, under ordinary conditions. On many farms it is the real solution of economical tractor power for heavy plowing work. The two 6–12s may be used as one tractor for plowing, disking, harrowing, and also belt work, and taken down in a few minutes into two separate tractors for cultivating, mowing, raking, etc."

The Duplex was truly revolutionary—but also too far ahead of its time. It did not sell well in the 1920s, although the concept of the tandem tractor would be revived and accepted following World War II.

1920s Model 6/12 advertisement
"$1,500,000 Have Been Spent in the Past Four Years to make Allis-Chalmers Farm Tractors Right for You," according to this ad.

LOOKING TO THE FUTURE

While Allis-Chalmers's early farm machines were not huge successes, Falk was still committed to building tractors. In 1917, he set up a separate tractor department and appointed Fred W. Kamm as manager. Two years later, Falk decided the department should have its own shop, which would produce the 10/18, 6/12, and a new prototype. At Falk's encouragement, the company's executive committee authorized a new foundry built in 1919 next to the tractor shop, allowing the foundry's castings to be moved efficiently into the shop. This foundry's capacity was 100 engine and transmission castings per day.

With this foundation, Allis-Chalmers was poised to enter into the next decade and create the first of its many successful and famous tractors.

1920s Duplex
The amazing Duplex combined two 6/12 tractors mounted back to back, offering farmers a pioneering tandem tractor for heavy-duty chores. The transmission controls of the two tractors were joined together, giving the machine a crude form of four-wheel drive. The Duplex was years ahead of its time—too far ahead, in fact, and few were built or sold. (Courtesy Norm Swinford)

CHAPTER 2

Building a Reputation for Tractors

MAIN PHOTO: **1926 Model E 20/35**
In the 1920s, the Model E 20/35 was Allis-Chalmers's flagship. When the model arrived in 1921, the company sold just 104 Model E tractors. But by 1927, it was selling 1,814 tractors annually; the following year it sold an incredible 4,867 Model Es.

INSET: **1919 Model 18/30 and 6/12 advertisement**
This ad promises "Over $3,000,000 spent in experimental and development work to make Allis-Chalmers Farm Tractors right."

The 1920s and 1930s were a bustling time for Allis-Chalmers, particularly for tractor engineering and sales. In 1926, Falk appointed Harry C. Merritt to the position of Tractor Division manager. A true "tractor man," Merritt began selling farm machinery when he was just seventeen years old. Along with Falk, Merritt was instrumental in making the Tractor Division an essential part of Allis-Chalmers's business. Both men were full of ideas for farm machinery, but also recognized that they needed to immediately focus on production, lower prices, and a more energetic field organization. Under Merritt's watch, the Tractor Division continued to increase sales even during the Great Depression. Between 1927 and 1930, the division's contribution to total company revenues rose from 7 percent to nearly 30 percent. By 1935, farm-equipment sales accounted for more than half of the company's production.

Still, the Great Depression was a tough time for Allis-Chalmers. The company stood firm, drawing strength from its longtime policy of diversification and the healthy new products and markets acquired in the 1920s. The economic crisis, however, did eventually impact Allis-Chalmers as it did many other farm-equipment makers. In 1933, Allis-Chalmers reported that billings had dropped to a low of $13 million. But Allis-Chalmers's rebound in 1934 and 1935 made headlines. In 1937, the firm reported revenues of more than $77 million; the Tractor Division had contributed $50 million of that total.

1918 Model 15/30 and 1919–1923 Model 18/30

Since farmers had difficulties steering the tricycle-type 10/18 and 6/12 tractors, Allis-Chalmers engineers set out to design four-wheel models. In 1918, the four-wheeled Model 15/30 was introduced for farmers seeking a three- or four-plow tractor. The 15/30 would become a landmark tractor for Allis-Chalmers, evolving into successful models that would carry the firm through the 1920s.

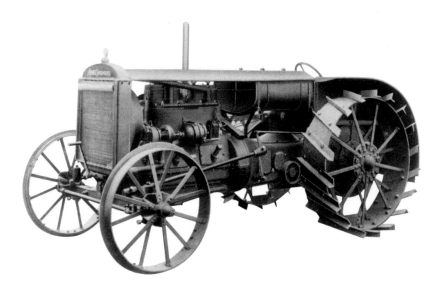

1921 Model E 18/30
The Model 15/30 was re-rated as the Model 18/30 in 1918, its first year of construction. (Courtesy Norm Swinford)

1927 Model E 20/35 duo
Twin "short-fender" Model E 20/35s prepare the Kansas soil for wheat with one-way wheatland plows.

The 15/30 had two forward speeds of up to 2.3 and 2.8 mph (3.68 and 4.5 kmh) and one reverse gear. It was advertised at 15 drawbar and 30 belt hp and had a drawbar pull of more than 3,000 pounds (1,350 kg).

In early field tests, the 15/30 produced dramatically more power than the factory had rated it at—a rare occurrence in the fledgling world of tractors—so Allis-Chalmers, starting later in 1919, renamed the tractor the Model 18/30. The 18/30 would also become known as the Model E, a name that stayed with the tractor despite its development into the later Models 20/35 and 25/40.

Whereas the 15/30 began with a sheet-metal radiator, at some point during the production run, the 18/30 had one of cast iron. The frame and chassis remained similar for both tractors, as did the price of $2,100. Their bodies were painted a deep green with yellow striping; their wheels were red.

The model featured an Allis-Chalmers four-cylinder, vertical, valve-in-head engine rated at 830 rpm. It had a 4.75x6.50-inch (118.75x162.50-mm) bore and stroke displacing 460.7 ci (7,546 cc). In low gear, the 6,150-pound (2,767-kg) tractor could travel at up to 2.31 mph (3.7 kmh).

Nebraska Test engineers evaluated 18/30 serial number 5729 in 1920. The tractor gave 20.19 drawbar and 33.41 belt hp—still more than Allis-Chalmers's 18/30 rating—and pulled 3,500 pounds (1,575 kg). The tractor used 3.29 gallons (12.5 liters) of fuel per hour.

An updated Model 18/30 (serial number 5929) was tested in 1921. The tractor used the same four-cylinder, vertical engine but now

The American farmer is buying some $200,000,000 worth of farm tools a year. . . .They are the best farm implements manufactured on the globe. They represent Yankee ingenuity at its highest, revolutionizing Yankee ingenuity.
—Barton W. Currie,
The Tractor, 1916

1926 Model E 20/35
Bold, colorful, and vibrant are all words that aptly describe the Model E's distinctive logo atop the radiator.

featured a Kingston Model L carburetor and Eisemann Model G-4 magneto. In low gear, the 18/30 pulled 3,510 pounds (1,580 kg). Nebraska Test engineers recorded 23.62 drawbar and 33.18 belt hp. The tractor had two forward speeds of 2.58 and 3.16 mph (4 and 5 kmh) and a reverse speed of 2.58 mph (4 kmh). It used 3.9 gallons (14.8 liters) of gas per hour.

The 18/30 was produced from 1918 to 1921, and 1,161 were built. Production started with serial number 5000 and ended with 6160. Serial numbers could be found on a metal tag on the transmission case.

1923–1930 MODEL E 20/35

Following the 18/30's Nebraska Test of 1921, Allis-Chalmers chose to again rename the tractor in 1923 as the Model 20/35, starting at serial number 6161.

Allis-Chalmers's tractor sales blossomed in the 1920s, and one of the key reasons was the firm's profitable redesign of the Model 20/35, launched in 1927. The redesign made the tractor more economical for farmers to buy, a key issue during the infamous Tractor Price War between Henry Ford's Fordson from Dearborn, Michigan, and International Harvester Company of Chicago, Illinois. Allis-Chalmers's board allowed Harry Merritt to buy parts outside the company if other manu-

1926 Model E 20/35
The early Model E 20/35 was known as the "long-fendered" version. The model was dramatically redesigned in 1927 to cut costs, and featured shorter fenders. This 20/35 is unique in being mounted on "road wheels." These big, wide rear wheels were especially popular on tractors that pulled road graders.

facturers could provide the same quality at lower prices. By substituting lighter parts of the same strength and quality for older ones and stripping non-essential parts, Allis-Chalmers was able to cut the price of the 20/35 from $1,950 to $1,295. Sales soared as a result. The new tractor was lighter than its predecessors, but still could do everything they had done—and it was easier to handle to boot.

The 20/35 used an Allis-Chalmers four-cylinder, vertical, I-head, valve-in-head engine. It retained the bore and stroke of the 18/30 at 4.75x6.50 inches (118.75x162.50 mm), displacing 460.7 ci (7,546 cc). Other standard features included a Kingston L 1.50-inch (37.5-mm) carburetor, Eisemann GS4 magneto, and Donaldson or Allis-Chalmers air cleaner.

Model 20/35 serial number 13620 was tested in Nebraska in 1928. The redesigned tractor weighed 7,095 pounds (3,193 kg) and boasted a maximum drawbar pull of 4,400 pounds (1,980 kg) in high gear and 33.20 drawbar hp. In power tests, the tractor used 5.02 gallons (19 liters) per hour and created 44.29 belt hp. It was rated at 930 rpm, and featured two forward speeds of 2.50 and 3.25 mph (4 and 5.2 kmh) and a reverse speed of 3.25 mph (5.2 mph).

The 20/35 was made from 1923 to 1930, when 18,025 were built, serial numbers 6161 to 24185. Serial numbers were located on a metal tag

1930s Model E 25/40
The 1934 brochure showed the Model E on both steel wheels and pneumatic rubber tires, which were introduced in 1929 with the Model U.

1934 Model E 25/40
When it was manufactured in 1934, this 25/40 was the largest Allis-Chalmers standard tractor made. Its Allis engine displaced a whopping 510.5 ci (8,362 cc) and brought 33.8 hp to the drawbar.

on the transmission case.

Throughout the 1920s, Allis-Chalmers focused its sales efforts on the 20/35. Tractor sales figures from 1921 to 1928 show the impact of Merritt's redesign suggestions: In 1921, the company sold just 104 tractors; in 1927, it sold 1,814 tractors; the following year it sold 4,867.

1921 Model L 12/20

Although manufactured by the Midwest firm of Indianapolis, Indiana, this Model L engine instead proudly displays the Allis-Chalmers name. The vertical, four-cylinder, valve-in-head engine displaced 280.6 ci (4,596 cc). Although the engine was built for gasoline, a special-order manifold for kerosene was available. The four cylinder walls were cast in pairs and featured push rods driven by cam followers. The cylinder head was one piece, as was the block.

1930–1936 MODEL E 25/40

Allis-Chalmers introduced a more powerful four-plow tractor with the launch of the Model E 25/40 in 1930. Engineers increased the bore from 4.75 to 5.00 inches (118.75 to 125 mm) in the four-cylinder, valve-in-head engine. A 5.25-inch (131.25-mm) bore was made available for thresher work. The rated speed also increased from 930 to 1,000 rpm. The tractor featured an Eisemann G4 magneto, Zenith C6EV carburetor, Donaldson air cleaner, and two forward speeds of 2.5 and 3.25 mph (4 and 5.2 kmh).

The E 25/40 was tested by Nebraska using distillate fuel in 1931, where it was referred to as the Model EK. The machine produced 27.69 drawbar and 47.00 brake hp. In low gear, it pulled 4,133 pounds (1,860 kg).

Allis-Chalmers produced 1,425 of the E 25/40 tractors from 1930 to 1936. Most of these tractors came with steel wheels; however, Allis-Chalmers also offered a limited number of tractors with pneumatic tires.

1920–1927 MODELS L 12/20 AND 15/25

Allis-Chalmers introduced the Model L 12/20 in 1920. The new tractor featured a Midwest four-cylinder, vertical, valve-in-head engine with a 4.125x5.25-inch (103x131.25-mm) bore and stroke displacing 280.6 ci (4,596 cc) and rated at 1,100 rpm. It had two forward speeds of 2.30 and 3.10 mph (3.68 and 5 kmh) and a reverse speed of 3.10 mph (5 kmh). The 12/20 also featured a Kingston Model L carburetor, Dixie Model 46-C magneto, and Taco No. 2 air cleaner.

This 4,400-pound (1,980-kg) tractor was built to handle a three-bottom plow under normal conditions and a two-bottom plow under most conditions. In the Nebraska Test of 1921, 12/20 serial number 20134 produced 33.18 belt hp and used 3.86 gallons (14.7 liters) of fuel per hour. In drawbar tests, the tractor pulled a maximum of 2,560 pounds (1,152 kg) in high gear and created 21.42 drawbar hp. The belt and drawbar tests prompted Allis-Chalmers to change the model designation to 15/25.

1921 Model L 12/20

Allis-Chalmers introduced the Model L 12/20 in 1920. Tested by Nebraska in 1921, it produced 21.42 drawbar and 33.18 belt hp, prompting the firm to change the model designation to 15/25.

When production ended in 1927, Allis-Chalmers had produced 1,705 of the Model L in 12/20 and 15/25 configurations, serial numbers 20001 to 21705. Serial numbers were located on a brass plate at the center of the tractor's rear fuel-tank support.

Building the Business

Tractor sales and profits allowed Allis-Chalmers to expand in the late 1920s. In 1925, Nichols & Shepard Company of Battle Creek, Michigan, began selling Allis-Chalmers's line, offering Allis-Chalmers vastly wider distribution. In 1928, Allis-Chalmers acquired the Monarch Tractor Corporation of Springfield, Illinois, which specialized in crawler tractors. To stay competitive with other farm-equipment companies, Allis-Chalmers needed to enter into the implement business so it acquired the La Crosse Plow Company of La Crosse, Wisconsin, in 1929. La Crosse manufactured plows, harrows, disks, drills, and cultivators.

Also in 1929, Allis-Chalmers signed a distribution contract for Canada with the Cockshutt Plow Company of Brantford, Ontario. It also signed an agreement whereby B. F. Avery & Sons of Louisville, Kentucky, distributed Allis-Chalmers equipment in Argentina.

1921 Model L 12/20
The 12/20 weighed a hefty 4,400 pounds (1,980 kg) and was designed to handle two to three plow bottoms. Only 705 were made before being superseded in 1929 by the Model U.

CHAPTER 3

The Debut of the Persian Orange Tractors

MAIN PHOTO: **1938 Model WC**
When Allis-Chalmers began production of the Model WC in 1933, it was the first tractor on the market to feature a "square" engine where the bore and stroke were equal. The WC was also unique in that much of it was constructed of high-tensile steel.

INSET: **1940s Allis-Chalmers dealer sign**
This 1940s vintage neon sign is extremely rare—and oddly does not include the hyphen in the company's name. It came from the Peterson Implement Company of Blooming Prairie, Minnesota. Owners Edwin and Larry Karg have never seen another one like it in all of their years of collecting Allis memorabilia.

According to Allis-Chalmers folklore, Tractor Division Manager Harry Merritt was visiting California in the late 1920s when he came upon a sight that stopped him in his tracks. He was amazed by acre upon acre of blooming wild poppies. He could see their vibrant orange color for miles. The story goes that the tractor man brought some poppies back to Milwaukee and asked the Pittsburgh Plate Glass Company to match the color. Merritt wanted his tractors painted in that beautiful poppy orange.

Allis-Chalmers made a series of color tests in various locations with different backgrounds. The Persian orange color was adopted in 1928 because it could always be distinguished from the landscape, even though the tractor might be covered with dirt and dust.

Upon their debut in 1929, Allis-Chalmers's Model U became the first in a long line of tractors and farm implements that boasted the Persian orange paint. The orange hue distinguished, and was credited for helping "sell," Allis-Chalmers equipment.

Interestingly, however, some foreign dealers and other organizations chose other colors for their Allis-Chalmers equipment. The distributor in India, for example, preferred a deep red, and African buyers often requested tan. Some southern U.S. states preferred canary yellow. And U.S. Army tractors were generally painted olive drab.

Still, it was Merritt's Persian orange color that became Allis-Chalmers's trademark.

1929–1931 United Tractor and 1929–1952 Model U

The interesting tale of the United tractor began when Henry Ford, disappointed with his Fordson tractor sales, moved his company's tractor assembly from the United States to Ireland. The firms that supplied equipment for the

1930 Model U

Starting in 1929, the year the Great Depression began, Allis built the United Tractor for the United Tractor and Equipment Distributors' Association of Chicago, Illinois. Allis distributors, meanwhile, sold the same tractor, rebadged as the Model U.

34

Fordson lost an important piece of their business as a result. To shore up losses, thirty-two of these suppliers formed the United Tractor and Equipment Distributors' Association of Chicago, Illinois. United contacted Allis-Chalmers, which agreed to build a "United Tractor" using the suppliers' equipment. The association sold the United Tractor for about $1,000. Allis-Chalmers distributors sold its identical—although rebadged—counterpart, the Allis-Chalmers Model U.

The United Tractor and Model U were powered by a four-cylinder, Continental S10, vertical, L-head engine. Its 4.25x5.00-inch (106.25x125-mm) bore and stroke displaced 283.7 ci (4,647 cc) and was rated at 1,200

rpm. The tractor featured a Kingston or Schebler HD 1.25-inch (31.25-mm) carburetor, Eisemann G4 magneto, Donaldson or Allis-Chalmers air cleaner, and steel wheels.

In high gear, the gasoline-powered United pulled 3,680 pounds (1,656 kg) with 25.63 drawbar hp. It featured 35.04 belt hp, using 4.18 gallons (15.9 liters) of gas per hour in the Nebraska Test of 1929.

The original version weighed 4,125 pounds (1,856 kg). It had three forward speeds of 2.33, 3.33, and 5 mph (3.7, 5.3, and 8 kmh) and a reverse speed of 2.66 mph (4.25 kmh). A later version featured a high-speed fourth gear.

The United tractor was produced from 1929 to 1932, when United went under. During that time, 7,404 were built, serial numbers U1 to U7404. Serial numbers were stamped on the rear axle housing beside the power takeoff (PTO).

Allis-Chalmers's Model U soldiered on after United's demise. In late 1932, Allis-Chalmers replaced the Continental engine with a UM engine made by the Waukesha Motor Company. The new four-cylinder, over-head-valve engine featured a 4.25x5.00-inch (106.25x125-mm) bore and stroke displacing 300.7 ci (4,927 cc). The engine was rated at 1,200 rpm. Allis-Chalmers produced 2,584 of the tractors with the 4.25-inch (106.25-mm) cylinder bore from 1932 to 1936.

In 1936, the U was equipped with a UM engine with a larger, 4.50-inch (112.50-mm) bore, expanding displacement to 318 ci (5,211 cc). Engineers also increased the tractor's rear wheels from 42 to 45 inches (105 to 112.50 cm) in diameter, and 28-inch (70-cm) rear tires on cast

**1930s Model U and 28–46
separator**
*When the Model U first debuted it was
often employed for powering threshing
machines. With 35 belt hp, the U had
power enough to spare for this job.*

1930 Model U
The Model U's four-cylinder, 283.7-ci (4,647-cc) Continental engine produced 25.63 drawbar and 35.04 belt hp at 1,300 rpm.

1935 Model U
The pair of curved metal pieces on both sides of the Model U provided support for both the gas tank and fenders—as well as perhaps keeping a little dust from reaching the operator.

1930 Model U
The Model U sported a wide, massive-appearing radiator with a different approach to retaining radiator cap.

wheels replaced the original 24-inch (60-cm) tires on spoke wheels. Allis-Chalmers produced 11,280 Model U tractors with the 4.50-inch bore until 1952. The first tractor with the larger cylinder bore was serial number U12001; the last serial number is unknown.

The U became the first tractor to offer low-pressure rubber tires as a standard feature. In spring 1932, Allis-Chalmers engineers mounted a pair of Firestone 12x48-inch (30x120-cm) airplane tires filled to a minimal 12 psi on a Model U owned by farmer Albert Schroeder of Waukesha County, Wisconsin. The experiment proved a success, so Allis-Chalmers put in motion plans to offer pneumatic tires. In summer 1932, the company staged public demonstrations to show farmers how the tractor fitted with air-filled tires worked. That October, Allis-Chalmers announced it would offer low-pressure pneumatic tires as standard equipment on the Model U.

Farmers, however, were skeptical of pneumatic tires. Other companies had introduced solid rubber tires and high-pressure truck tires, but they did not perform well under farming's rigors. To convince them that its low-pressure pneumatic tires would perform, Allis-Chalmers devel-

TOP PHOTO: **1930s Model U**
The Model U was the first tractor to offer pneumatic rubber tires as a standard feature. In spring 1932, Allis engineers mounted a pair of Firestone 12x48-inch (30x120-cm) airplane tires on a Model U. The experiment proved a great success, and suddenly steel wheels were largely obsolete. By 1938, most farm tractors were delivered equipped with rubber tires.

BOTTOM PHOTO: **"Air Tired Farm Tractor Record Run"**
Allis-Chalmers promoted its new pneumatic technology by making a record run from Milwaukee to Chicago—88 1/10 miles in a mere five hours and one minute! Pity the poor driver, who looks as though he's ready to return to the ease of merely plowing from dawn to dusk.

oped high-speed fourth gears and held tractor races around the country. An estimated one million people witnessed the tractor races in 1933, and the races were so popular that they were held for several years thereafter.

On September 17, 1933, famed automobile racer Barney Oldfield caught everyone's attention by driving a Model U on pneumatic tires to a record speed of 64.28 mph (102.85 kmh) in Dallas, Texas. This was the first of three speed tests, and the official record was later increased to 67.87 mph (108.59 kmh). Such speeds were obviously not practical on the farm. However, the tests proved that rubber-tired tractors had surpassed the slow, steel-wheeled types. The rubber-tired farm tractor was one of the key developments that marked a turning point in Allis-Chalmers's tractor history.

Allis-Chalmers's low-pressure-tire development was considered a breakthrough. A key to making the rubber tires work was the addition of flexible casings, allowing the tire tread to spread out and make better contact with the ground and helping to better distribute the load. As a result, later tractors would provide greater tractive efficiency—the ratio between the power at the drawbar and the power produced by the

1930s Firestone advertisement

Allis's Harry Merritt was a family friend of Harvey Firestone of Firestone Rubber Company fame. Merritt furnished a Model U to Firestone for use on his farm in Ohio. Firestone was intrigued with the possibilities of using rubber on the farm and worked with Merritt in figuring out how to equip tractors with pneumatic tires.

1930s Model U cartoon

When Allis-Chalmers first offered pneumatic rubber tires in the 1930s, a revolution in farming arrived—not to mention a revolution in comfort for farmers! Firestone Rubber Company worked with Allis in developing tires for agricultural use, and by the mid-1930s, "air tires" were replacing the old steel-cleated wheels on everyone's tractors, except for certain diehard old-timers. This cartoon poked fun at rubber tires and the promises of "faster farming" that accompanied them.

1930s Model U tractor race

Allis organized tractor races at county and state fairs across North America to display the speeds possible with the new rubber-tired Model U. Here, famed race-car driver and Allis promoter Barney Oldfield leads two other Us around a horse-racing dirt-track. Oldfield always won his race—it was written into his contract.

1930 Model U Trackson crawler
The Trackson Company of Milwaukee, Wisconsin, offered a conversion kit that transformed a wheel-type tractor into a crawler, such as with this Model U. The crawler's four-speed transmission allowed speeds from 2.2 to 9.5 mph (3.5–15.2 kmh).

ABOVE: **1930 Model U Trackson crawler**
Trackson was contracted in 1928 to design an Allis crawler, but Allis bought the Monarch Tractor Corporation of Springfield, Illinois, that same year before Trackson could complete its machine.

LEFT: **1930 Model U Trackson crawler**
The steering wheel belies the origins of this Model U as a standard wheeled tractor rather than a crawler. The Trackson conversion kit provided the treads.

1935 Model UC
Steel wheels were still in vogue in 1935 when this UC was built. The steel wheels were four times as efficient as rubber tires, offering 4.1 percent versus 16.5 percent slippage.

1935 Model UC
The UC was manufactured from 1930 through 1941, right in the midst of the Great Depression.

engine. Previously, tractors with steel lugs used much of their power to push lugs into the ground and pull them out again. Tractors with low-pressure rubber tires required about half as much power as tractors with steel wheels and lugs. This enabled farmers to use smaller-horsepower engines that saved about a gallon (3.8 liters) of fuel per hour.

In addition to the power issue, the new rubber tires provided farmers a smoother ride, greater speed in the field, and less damage to barnyards than their steel-wheeled counterparts. Rubber tires soon caught on with farmers. In 1935, *Farm Implement News* estimated that between 15,000 and 20,000 farmers bought tractor tires in 1934.

1930–1941 ALL-CROP/MODEL UC

Allis-Chalmers started the 1930s off with production of its new tricycle row-crop All-Crop tractor, later known as the Model UC. The All-Crop was created in response to the growing market for general-purpose row-crop tractors as made popular by International Harvester's Farmall.

The gas-powered All-Crop featured a four-cylinder Continental engine with a 4.25x5.00-inch (106.25x125-mm) bore and stroke displacing 283.7 ci (4,647 cc). The engine was rated at 1,200 rpm. The tractor included a Kingston or Zenith C5 E 1.25-inch (31.25-mm) carburetor,

1935 Model UC
The UC was Allis's solution for a row-crop unit that would allow farmers to more readily cultivate their crops. This one is on rubber tires.

1930s Model UC
The Model UC was originally known as the "All-Crop" tractor—a name similar in evocative style to International Harvester's Farmall. This tractor was pulling both a rotary hoe and a corrugated roller in young corn in Indiana.

1930s Model UC
This UC on all steel wheels was being operated on an Indiana farm, turning the soil under with a three-bottom plow.

Eisemann GL4 magneto, and a Vortox, Donaldson, or Allis-Chalmers air cleaner.

Model UC serial number UC 217 was tested at Nebraska in 1931. The test measured 24.98 drawbar hp with the tractor pulling 3,763 pounds (1,693 kg). Power at the belt was 36.09 hp, with the tractor using 4.09 gallons (15.5 liters) of gas per hour. The All-Crop/Model UC had three forward speeds of 2.33, 3.33, and 5 mph (3.7, 5.3, and 8 kmh), and a reverse speed of 2.66 mph (4.25 kmh).

Beginning with serial number 1269 in 1933, Allis-Chalmers built several more UC tractors with its own four-cylinder UM engine. The engine measured 4.375x5.00 inches (109.375x125 mm) bore and stroke, displacing 300.7 ci (4,925 cc). The UC tractor featuring this engine was produced until 1936, ending with serial number UC2281.

In 1935, the UC was tested at Nebraska with both steel wheels and rubber tires. On steel, 24.17 drawbar and 34.09 belt hp were recorded, and the tractor pulled 3,422 pounds (1,540 kg). On rubber, the UC pulled 2,593 pounds (1,167 kg). Maximum power was 28.85 drawbar hp.

In 1937, Allis-Chalmers began producing a Cane version of the UC.

ABOVE: **1933 Model WC**
This 1933 model was the nineteenth WC manufactured. On steel wheels, the WC weighed 3,190 pounds (1,436 kg); rubber tires brought the tractor's weight up to 3,792 pounds (1,706 kg).

LEFT: **1933 Model WC**
The vertical four-cylinder Allis I-head engine with an even 4.00x4.00-inch (100x100-mm) bore and stroke displaced 201.1 ci (3,294 cc).

It made 1,540 of these tractors until production ended in 1953. A UC Industrial model was also offered from 1937 to 1947.

1933–1948 MODEL WC AND 1937–1951 MODEL WF

Whereas the Model U introduced farmers to pneumatic tires, Allis-Chalmers's Model WC was the industry's first row-crop model to be tested at the University of Nebraska with such tires. The WC also had the distinction of being the first tractor to feature a "square" engine where the bore and stroke were equal. In addition, the WC was unique in that much of it was constructed of high-tensile steel.

Allis-Chalmers began producing the Model WC in 1933. With its rubber tires, this fast, two-plow tractor quickly became one of the company's all-time best sellers. Between 1933 and 1948, Allis-Chalmers produced 178,202 of these tractors, serial numbers WC1 to WC178202. The serial numbers could be found stamped on the rear of the differential housing near the tractor's oil fill plug.

The WC was equipped with an Allis-Chalmers four-cylinder, I-head engine rated at 1,300 rpm. It featured a 4.00x4.00-inch (100x100-mm) bore and stroke displacing 201.1 ci (3,294 cc). Other features included a Kingston carburetor, Bendix-Scintilla C4 magneto, and United air cleaner.

1934 Allis-Chalmers catalog
Allis's new Model WC graced the cover of the firm's 1934 catalog.

1933 Model WC
Tested by Nebraska in 1934, the steel-wheeled WC rated 14.36 drawbar and 21.48 belt hp. The rubber-tired counterpart featured 19.17 drawbar hp.

The WC featured three forward speeds of 2.50, 3.50 and 4.75 mph (4, 5.6, and 7.6 kmh). A fourth gear allowing a top speed of 9.2 mph (14.7 kmh) was recommended for the rubber-tired version only. In reverse, the WC could travel at up to 2 mph (3.2 kmh). The fourth gear and rubber tires allowed farmers to do field work in about three-quarters the time traditionally required. The WC also helped farmers improve fuel savings.

In 1934, Nebraska tested the WC on both steel wheels and rubber tires. Distillate fuel was used in each test. The steel-wheeled WC rated 14.36 drawbar and 21.48 belt hp and pulled 1,921 pounds (864 kg).

The rubber-tired counterpart featured 19.17 drawbar hp, pulling

"Believe it or not" the Full 2-Plow Model "WC" has—

Removable Cylinder Sleeves | Oil Filter Air Cleaner | Four Speeds Forward | Platform | Anti-Friction Bearings Thru-out | Inserted Valve Seats | Burns Gasoline or Kerosene

1,735 pounds (781 kg). With steel wheels, the WC weighed 3,190 pounds (1,436 kg); rubber tires brought the tractor's weight up to 3,792 pounds (1,706 kg).

The WC was tested by Nebraska again in 1938 using distillate and gas fuel. Again, the tractor was tested on both steel wheels and rubber tires. On distillate, the steel-wheeled WC produced 18.72 drawbar and 25.45 belt hp, and pulled 2,599 pounds (1,170 kg). On rubber, 20.41 drawbar hp was noted. The rubber-tired WC pulled 3,054 pounds (1,374 kg).

On gasoline, the steel-wheeled WC produced 22.29 drawbar and 29.93 belt hp, pulling 2,941 pounds (1,323 kg). Its rubber-tired counterpart recorded 24.16 drawbar hp. It pulled 3,136 pounds (1,411 kg).

In 1937, Allis-Chalmers developed the WF, a standard-tread version of the WC for farmers who did not want or could not use a row-crop tractor. The low, narrow WF also could be easily modified for orchard work. The orchard model had special fenders and a low operator's station.

Both tractors used the same Allis-Chalmers W engine with 4.00x4.00-inch (100x100-mm) bore and stroke. Like the WC, the WF was rated at 1,300 rpm. The tractors were identical with the exception of the tread design, and this may be why the WF was not tested in Nebraska. However, it could also be attributed to the fact that the Nebraska Tractor Test ceased in 1941 for the duration of World War II and did not resume until 1946.

Between 1937 and 1940, Allis-Chalmers produced 1,900 WF tractors, serial numbers WF4 through WF1903. The tractor underwent restyling in 1940 with serial number 1904. The WF did not sell as well as the popular WC, and due in part to the lack of materials because of the war, no WF tractors were built in 1943. Allis-Chalmers resumed production in 1944 and built the last WF (serial number 8353) in 1951.

hrow Out
elt Pulley

Cut Steel
Hardened Gears

Fenders

1930s Model WC cutaway
"Believe it or not," taunts this 1930s WC brochure while showing off the innards of the latest and greatest Allis tractor.

1936 Model WC
The unstyled WC was one of the most popular tractors Allis-Chalmers ever produced. More than 178,000 of these tractors were produced from 1933 through 1948.

Top photo: **1936 Model WC**
Farmers loved the WC tractor's simplicity and ruggedness.

Bottom photo: **1935 Allis-Chalmers catalog**
A Model WC worked the fields on the cover of this full-line catalog.

1938 Model WC
This unstyled WC is mounted with skeleton rear wheels and a wide front axle. This was one of the most economical tractors the company ever produced.

ABOVE: **1948 Model WC**
The WC's new streamlined styling found a place in farmer's hearts, and production was increased 12 percent in 1939 to meet demand.

RIGHT: **1948 Model WC**
Streamlined styling came to the Model WC in 1938. Its lines were cleaner and more curvaceous than the unstyled WC, and it projected an image of capability.

ABOVE: **1930s Model WC brochure**
"Family Farming" is the motto for this WC catalog, with Sis at the wheel of the family's new pride and joy.

LEFT: **1938 Model WC**
The exhaust exited through a short, straight pipe, which was extremely loud. Later models had the exhaust pipe routed up through the hood and ending with a muffler.

1937 Model A

When this Model A was manufactured in 1937, it incorporated the engine of Allis's famous and hugely popular Model E 25/40, displacing 460.7 ci (7,546 cc). The A is a nice tractor to drive. It's heavy, but steers well and has loads of low-end torque.

1936–1942 MODEL A

The Model A was produced from 1936 to 1942, serial numbers 25701 to 26925. Allis-Chalmers produced 1,225 of these tractors, but the Model A was never tested by Nebraska.

The Model A incorporated the engine of the venerable Model E 25/40. For the Model A, the 460.7-ci (7,546-cc) engine was rated at 1,000 rpm. The tractor produced 33 drawbar and 44 belt hp. This rating was later increased to 39.7 drawbar and 51.2 belt hp.

1937–1957 MODEL B

Most tractors of the 1930s were built for larger acreages. So, to fill the need for smaller farms, Allis-Chalmers developed the Model B. With production starting in 1937, the B would be built for twenty years, with the last tractor made in 1957. Allis-Chalmers produced 118,500 of these tractors.

The B cost just $495, which was significantly less than Allis-Chalmers's larger tractors. It featured a four-cylinder Allis-Chalmers vertical, I-head engine with a 3.25x3.50-inch (81.25x87.50-mm) bore and stroke displacing 116.1 ci (1,902 cc). It was rated at 1,400 rpm.

In the Nebraska Test of 1938, the Model B provided fuel economy of 11.14 hp hours per gallon (3.8 liters) with 14 hp. At 12.97 drawbar and 15.68 belt hp, the B pulled 1,074 pounds (483 kg). Distillate fuel was used in the test.

ABOVE, LEFT: **1939 Model B**
First introduced in 1937, full production of the Model B didn't begin until the following year—but then continued for an amazing twenty years. When new, this 1939 model sold for $495. Allis created the Model B for smaller farms as most tractors of the 1930s were built for larger acreages.

ABOVE, RIGHT: **1939 Model B**
The B boasted an arched front axle and high rear-axle clearance, making it a popular tractor with truck farmers and nursery growers. It weighed just 2,100 pounds (945 kg) and was designed for one-row planters and cultivators.

LEFT: **1940s Model B brochure**
The shadows of four draft horses loom above the modern-day iron horse on the cover of this 1940s Allis catalog.

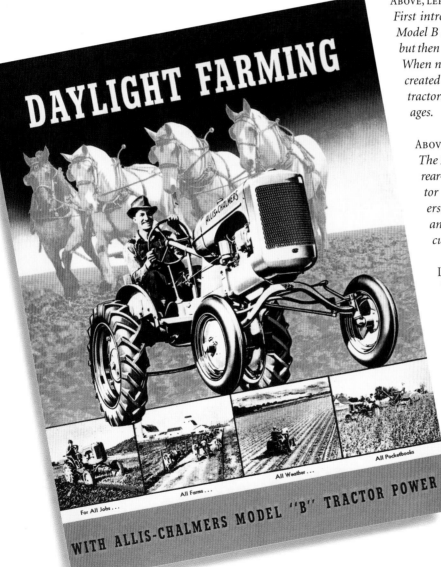

ABOVE: **1940 Model B**
List price of the B when introduced in 1937 was $495; the optional rear-mounted belt pulley and PTO added $35. An array of implements tailor-made for the B was available.

LEFT: **1940 Model B**
Most Model Bs came equipped with rubber tires, but due to the rubber shortage during World War II, this 1940 model was mounted on steel wheels.

Count the savings in corn and cash.
—Allis-Chalmers ad, 1955

1947 Allis-Chalmers fair display

Allis-Chalmers showed off its new Model B—as well as its other tractors and implements—to state and country fair-goers everywhere. Here, at the Minnesota State Fair in 1947, Machinery Hill was crowned by this lineup of Bs and a wide array of implements.

The little tractor featured three forward speeds of 2.50, 4.00, and 7.75 mph (4, 6.4, and 12.4 kmh) and a reverse speed of 2.00 mph (3.2 kmh). Some of the early B tractors featured steel wheels, but most had rubber tires. Other features included a Fairbanks-Morse FR4B magneto, Handy governor, Zenith 61A7 carburetor, Rockford clutch, and an upholstered seat.

The B weighed just 2,100 pounds (945 kg), and its lightweight design influenced future tractor designs by both Allis-Chalmers and its competitors. The tractor was designed for one-row planters and cultivators. Because of its high-arch front axle and rear-axle clearance, the B was popular with truck farmers and nursery growers. The front axle could be set for 43- or 50-inch-tread (107.5- or 125-cm) spacings. For an additional price, the front axle could be adjusted to provide ten spacings from 38 to 60 inches (95–150 cm). Farmers could change the rear wheel treads by adjusting rims or clamps and reversing the rear wheels.

There was an extensive line of implements compatible with the Model B. Suppliers designed numerous attachments that enhanced the tractor's versatility for farmers with small acreages. The tractor also featured an optional hydraulic lift, a first for Allis-Chalmers.

Allis-Chalmers proudly reported that by 1940 the Model B had not only permeated the U.S. market, but also was popular in Europe, Africa, Australia, and South America.

1938–1941 MODEL RC

In 1938, Allis-Chalmers put an enlarged Model B engine into the WC chassis and created the Model RC. The RC was designed for farmers

1939 Model RC
With the RC, Allis-Chalmers attempted to build an economy tractor. An enlarged Model B engine was mounted into the WC chassis to create the RC. However, the price difference wasn't large enough to attract many buyers, since the WC was more powerful for only a few more dollars. This was just the sixth RC built.

1939 Model RC
The seat of the RC was offset to the right for better visibility.

using two-row plows and cultivators. Because this tractor had a WC chassis, farmers also could use implements designed for the WC.

The revised B engine featured a bore and stroke of 3.375x3.50 inches (84.375x87.50 mm), displacing 125.2 ci (2,051 cc). In its 1939 Nebraska Test, it was rated at 15.25 drawbar and 18.21 belt hp, and pulled 1,551 pounds (698 kg).

With its WC chassis, however, the RC was heavier than it needed to be, weighing 2,495 pounds (1,123 kg) on steel and 3,204 pounds (1,442 kg) on rubber tires. It was also costly to produce. With an eye toward reducing assembly costs, Allis-Chalmers engineers redesigned the body, thus creating the Model C, a tractor for the 1940s.

The company produced 5,501 of the RC tractors until production ended in 1941. The tractors bore serial numbers 4 through 5504.

1940–1950 MODEL C

The Model RC served as an interim model while Allis-Chalmers engineers fine-tuned the new Model C, which debuted in 1940. The C was marketed as a competitively priced two-plow tractor. It was lighter than the RC and less costly for Allis-Chalmers to produce.

This tricycle-type tractor featured its own line of front-mounted implements. Front-mounted implements were promoted as enhancing the operator's visibility. The 80 Series cultivators for the C were offered in several models and styles for different crops and tillage practices. The tractor could use one- and two-way pick-up plows and a semi-mounted disc plow. However, the tractor also could use rear-mounted implements that were interchangeable with the Model B. A Cane version was also offered.

Engineers equipped the C with a four-cylinder, Allis-Chalmers I-head engine with a 3.375x3.50-inch (84.375x87.50-mm) bore and stroke displacing 125 ci (2,048 cc) and rated at 1,500 rpm. Also included was a Zenith 61-AJ-7, 0.875-inch (21.875-mm) carburetor, Donaldson air cleaner, and Fairbanks-Morse FM-J4B magneto. The tractor had three forward speeds of 2.50, 3.75, and 7.50 mph (4, 6, and 12 kmh), and one reverse speed of 2.75 mph (4.4 kmh).

1950 Model C
This Model C has been mounted with an aftermarket Sherman two-speed transmission. This not only made the tractor 8 inches (20 cm) longer, but it also transformed the standard four-speed gearbox into a much more flexible eight-speed transmission.

1950 Model C
The aftermarket Sherman two-speed auxiliary gearbox fit in with the regular transmission and doubled the number of forward speeds to eight and reverse speeds to two.

The C featured 4x15-inch (10x37.50-cm) front and (22.50x60-cm) rear tires. It was offered with adjustable front axles. Vegetable farmers and others could also get the Model C with a single front wheel.

The C was evaluated in two Nebraska Tests in 1940, rating it on distillate and gasoline fuels. In the distillate test, the 3,205-pound (1,442-kg) C recorded 15.96 drawbar and 19.40 belt hp. It pulled 2,368 pounds (1,066 kg).

The gas-powered model rated 18.43 drawbar and 23.30 belt hp. It pulled 2,352 pounds (1,058 kg).

The company produced 84,020 Model C tractors from 1940 to 1950.

REFLECTING ON AN ERA OF GROWTH

Allis-Chalmers experienced steady growth during the 1920s. In 1927, the Tractor Division generated $2.26 million in sales, nearly 7 percent of the company's total revenues of $33.3 million. By 1929, the Tractor Division—which now included crawler tractors and farm implements—generated $10.9 million in sales, contributing 24 percent of the company's $45.3 million revenues.

In the 1930s, Allis-Chalmers witnessed changes to the Tractor Division's management. In 1930, Harry Merritt appointed W. A. Roberts to manage sales, while Merritt returned to a focus on engineering. Roberts joined the company in 1924 as a sales representative in the Tractor Division's Wichita, Kansas, office. He was transferred to Canada in 1926. Roberts resigned in 1928 to enter a partnership in a farm-equipment dealer-distributorship. He now returned to Allis-Chalmers to become the tractor sales manager.

In 1932, General Otto Falk became chairman of the board. Falk was the man who had been responsible for championing the tractor cause and making the Tractor Division an integral part of Allis-Chalmers. Max W. Babb succeeded Falk as president. Babb had joined Allis-Chalmers in 1904 as an attorney. He also served as the company's vice president from 1913 to 1932.

Between 1934—the last year of the Depression—and 1941, the Tractor Division's sales grew steadily. The company reported that its net annual sales for 1941 were thirteen times greater than those of 1934. The company as a whole recorded sales of nearly $122 million and net profits of almost $5.8 million in 1941. As the company history, *Pioneer Power*, stated, "The millions represented in this increase reflect the energy of the period and go far beyond the posted figures marking those gypsy years of the early twenties."

The 1940s also witnessed the loss of the man who got the Tractor Division off the ground. General Otto Falk passed away on May 21, 1940. Babb now succeeded him as chairman of the board.

W. C. Buchanan, a steel-industry executive, soon succeeded Babb as the company's president. Due to illness, however, Buchanan resigned a few months later.

Walter Geist, who served as Allis-Chalmers vice president, became president in May 1942. Interestingly, Geist started as an errand boy in the company's sawmill department in 1909. At the same time, he attended night school and university extension courses. Geist acquired engineering knowledge from his experience at Allis-Chalmers, and is credited for originating the multiple V-belt drive principle for power transmission.

Dynamic duo, 1930s
Allis-Chalmers's sales manager Bill Roberts tries out the seat of a new crawler while Harry C. Merritt watches at the rear.

In 1941, Harry Merritt—the man who built the Tractor Division's reputation and introduced the famed Persian orange trademark color—retired due to poor health. Allis-Chalmers reported that he would continue to contribute his ideas to the farm-implement industry. He was succeeded by W. A. Roberts, formerly the company's general sales manager. Roberts became division vice president in 1944.

CHAPTER 4

Monarch and Allis-Chalmers Crawlers

MAIN PHOTO: **1937 Model MO**
The orchard version of the Allis-Chalmers Monarch Model M was known as the Model MO. Made in both narrow- or wide-tread versions, this is the wide-tread MO.

INSET: **1919 Monarch 18/30 Neverslip advertisement**
From its inception in 1913, Monarch offered a wide variety of crawlers, including the evocatively named Neverslip.

Backed by its strong tractor sales and profits in the late 1920s, Allis-Chalmers sought to expand its tractor range, and in 1928, it acquired the Monarch Tractor Corporation of Springfield, Illinois. Since its establishment in 1913, Monarch had grown to be a leader in the manufacture of crawler-type tractors.

The Monarch Tractor Company began in Watertown, Wisconsin, building crawlers, such as its 6/10 Lightfoot and Model M 12/20 Neverslip. The firm was reorganized in 1925 as the Monarch Tractor Corporation, now based in Springfield. Despite its successful line of light- and heavy-duty crawlers, the firm was in dire straits by the late 1920s. Allis-Chalmers purchased the company on February 27, 1928, for a mere $500,000.

The Monarch acquisition brought to Allis-Chalmers 35-, 50-, and 75-hp crawlers that served as the base for the company's future crawler tractors. Over the years, Allis-Chalmers would expand the Springfield Works several times. Springfield products would play essential roles in both World War I and II and in the growth of Allis-Chalmers in the United States and abroad.

Allis-Chalmers carried over Monarch's three crawler models after acquisition of Monarch in 1928. The three Monarchs were the Model C 25/35, which became the Allis-Chalmers Monarch 35; the Model H 6 Ton, which became the Allis-Chalmers Monarch 50; and the flagship Model F 10 Ton, which became the Allis-Chalmers Monarch 75.

1929–1943 MONARCH 35/MODELS K AND SPECIAL K

Allis-Chalmers built the Monarch 35 with an Allis-Chalmers four-cylinder, vertical, I-head engine. Rated at 930 rpm, it featured a 4.75x6.50-inch (118.75x162.50-mm) bore and stroke, displacing 460 ci (7,538 cc). The crawler included a Zenith 6C carburetor, Eisemann G4 magneto, and Allis-Chalmers governor and air cleaner.

The Monarch 35 was tested by Nebraska in 1929. This 10,680-pound (4,806-kg) machine featured three forward gears. In low gear, the gas-

1920s Monarch 20/30 Industrial

A Monarch 20/30 crawler hauls an estimated 44 tons (39,600 kg) of fresh-cut lumber from the woods of Michigan at a speed of 4 mph (6.4 kmh).

powered crawler had a maximum drawbar pull of 8,450 pounds (3,803 kg). The test tractor was not equipped with a belt pulley so Nebraska did not conduct a belt power test. Drawbar power was rated at 40.99 hp.

Allis-Chalmers's Model K debuted in 1929 and eventually replaced the venerable Monarch 35. The company built 9,468 of these 11,670-pound (5,252-kg) Model K machines until 1943.

The tractor was powered by a four-cylinder, valve-in-head engine that could run on either gasoline or kerosene. The 5.25x6.50-inch (131.25x162.50-mm) bore and stroke displaced 511 ci (8,370 cc). The K had three forward and one reverse gears. In low gear in the Nebraska Test, the gas-fueled Special K pulled a whopping 8,865 pounds (3,989 kg) and rated 47.87 drawbar and 55.24 belt/PTO hp.

Allis-Chalmers said this crawler was capable of pulling five 14-inch (35-cm) plows under any condition, or driving the largest grain threshers on the belt. In its *Agricultural Catalog 35*, the company noted the tractor was a good investment for large farms, orchards, and other operations where "peak loads are heavy and day and night operation is often necessary to get the work done on time." The company added that the tractor, "because of its unusual strength and stamina, has won the approval of government officials; state, county and municipal highway officials; and contractors in all parts of the world."

1928–1931 MONARCH 50
The Monarch 50 was equipped with a four-cylinder, vertical, I-head engine with a 5.25x6.50-inch (131.25x162.50-mm) bore and stroke displacing 563 ci (9,222 cc) and rated at 1,000 rpm. Other features included an Eisemann GV4 magneto and Zenith C-6 carburetor.

Tested by Nebraska in 1930, it weighed 15,100 pounds (6,849 kg). In low gear, the 50 pulled 10,573 pounds (4,796 kg). Power was rated at 53.28 drawbar and 62.18 belt hp.

1926–1931 MONARCH 75
The Monarch 75 featured a Beaver–LeRoi four-cylinder, valve-in-head engine with 6.50x7.00-inch (162.50x175-mm) bore and stroke, displacing 929 ci (15,217

1930 Model 75 advertisement
"As a product of Allis-Chalmers the Monarch is truly a remarkable accomplishment," states this ad for the Allis-Chalmers Monarch 75.

1932 Model K

Unusual for crawlers, this Model K was turned with a steering wheel rather than the traditional levers. The steering wheel could only be turned enough to release the clutch on each side. A change was made from steering wheel to lever steering in 1935 at serial number K4451. The steering wheel was a feature that carried over from the Monarch tractor line that Allis bought.

1932 Model K

The engine of the K developed 48 drawbar hp. The crawler weighed a massive 11,000 pounds (4,950 kg).

cc) and rated at 850 rpm. Other features included a Zenith L7T carburetor, American Bosch ZR4 magneto, and United air cleaner.

The 21,700-pound (9,765-kg) crawler was tested by Nebraska as the Monarch Model F 10 Ton in 1927. The 75 pulled 20,050 pounds (9,023 kg) at 78.17 drawbar hp. Since the crawler was not equipped with a belt pulley, no belt power tests were conducted.

Allis-Chalmers also made a 75 Logger version, featuring a heavy steel plate to protect the radiators.

1931–1942 MODELS L AND LO

Allis-Chalmers developed the Model L crawler to replace the aging Monarch 75 in 1931. By the time the last L tractor was produced in 1942, Allis-Chalmers had built 3,357 of these gasoline-powered crawlers.

The Model L was tested in Nebraska in 1932 powered by an Allis-Chalmers six-cylinder, I-head engine. The engine featured a 5.25x6.50-inch (131.25x162.50-mm) bore and stroke displacing 844 ci (13,825 cc) and operating at 1,050 rpm.

The crawler featured removable cast-iron cylinder sleeves that helped provide long life and cost little to replace. The crawler also boasted automatic pressure lubrication of all working parts: The oil filter cleaned the engine's oil supply every seven minutes.

An LO "Oil" version was also offered. The "Oil" engines—which were also eventually available in KO, SO, and WKO models—were spark-ignition engines fitted with fuel injection, allowing them to burn diesel fuel. With the "Oil" engine, fuel economy was dramatically improved.

The big crawler weighed 22,027 pounds (9,912 kg), and was advertised at 60 drawbar and 80 belt hp. In the Nebraska Test, it was rated at 76.01 drawbar and 91.93 belt hp. In low gear, it pulled 15,086 pounds (6,789 kg). It had six forward and two reverse gears.

The L could handle large plowing units and belt-driven farm machinery, and a broad range of accessory equipment was available. "Despite its size and power, it is in no sense ponderous, and can be handled and maneuvered with the ease and simplicity of the smallest tractor," reported the company's *Agricultural Catalog 35*. The crawler's tread measured 68 inches (170 cm) from center to center of the tracks. The tractor itself was a monstrous 12 feet, 9 inches (382.5 cm) long and 7 feet, 7 inches (227.5 cm) wide.

Stories of the Model L's efficient service came out of the construction camps along the $325-million Mississippi River levee project of the early 1930s. "By July, there were 86 Model L's between Cairo, Ill., and the Gulf, plus a sprinkling of A-C Model 35's," noted the July 1947 edition of *WE of Allis-Chalmers*, the company's house magazine.

Geared to the Ground.
—Cletrac Motor Plow
ad slogan, 1910s

1932–1942 MODEL M

The Model M debuted in 1932 as a new, lighter-weight crawler targeted at smaller jobs and operations. At 6,620 pounds (2,979 kg), the M weighed less than the L or K. It became a popular model, with 14,524 tractors eventually produced up until 1942.

The M was available as a standard or orchard crawler. The standard model could pull three to four plows or the heaviest combine.

The M was equipped with a four-cylinder Allis-Chalmers engine with a 4.375x5.00-inch (109.375x125-mm) bore and stroke displacing 300 ci (4,914 cc) and rated at 1,200 rpm. It featured four forward gears and one reverse.

Tested at Nebraska in 1935, the M rated 28.66 drawbar and 35.05 belt/PTO hp. It pulled 3,450 pounds (1,553 kg).

Like the L, the M featured removable iron cylinder liners. The engine had valve seats of tool steel to avoid valve grinding. It also featured full-force feed lubrication through drilled passages in the crankcase, crankshaft, and connecting rods.

The M was fitted with an oversize tubular radiator with a water pump and a fan mounted on a single shaft. Allis-Chalmers reported that the M's fixed-jet carburetor would work well at various angles at which the tractor might be tilted. The model also featured a high-tension airplane-type magneto.

The orchard model used the same engine, transmission, and tracks as the standard tractor, but it featured a lower radiator, hood, seat, and

LEFT: **1937 Model M**
This Model M crawler rolled off the assembly line in 1937. It featured the 50-inch-gauge (125-cm) wider tread. A narrow tread, 40-inch-gauge (100-cm) version was also available.

BELOW: **1937 Model MO**
This wide-tread Model MO was designed for orchard work, hence the "O" suffix to its designation. Otherwise, it was similar to the standard M. The crawler featured a low operator station to protect the driver from being hit by branches and fruit.

controls. The orchard tractor's fenders were designed to protect trees, branches, and vines from injury. Allis-Chalmers reported that the fenders allowed for much closer work, "thus eliminating offset hitches on many of the tools used for cultivation in this kind of crop and allowing for much better control of the implements."

The tractor's variation of speeds enabled the operator to accomplish more work per day as the speed could be adjusted to the particular implement or load. Moreover, the steering clutch control feature allowed the tractor to turn in close quarters. Other features included electric lights and starter, and a PTO to power sprayers, compressors, and cutters.

"Fruit growers are urged to inspect the Model M and the equipment designed to go with it, for only by seeing it can its many splendid features be fully appreciated," noted Allis-Chalmers's catalog.

The Line of Quality.
—Allis-Chalmers
catalog slogan, 1940s

1937–1942 MODELS S AND SO

Allis-Chalmers produced the Model S and SO from 1937 to 1942, serial numbers 3 through 1227. These crawlers featured a four-cylinder engine with 5.75x6.50-inch (143.75x162.50-mm) bore and stroke displacing 675 ci (11,057 cc) and rated at 1,050 rpm.

Tested by Nebraska in 1937, the SO's oil engine used mechanical fuel injection with electric-spark ignition. The 20,100-pound (9,045-kg) SO rated 62.39 drawbar and 74.82 belt hp. It pulled 16,732 pounds (7,529 kg). The SO featured five forward speeds.

The gasoline S rated 69 drawbar hp and weighed 20,330 pounds (9,149 kg).

1937–1943 MODELS WS, WK, AND WKO

Allis-Chalmers's WKO diesel crawler carried an Allis-Chalmers four-cylinder engine with a Deco fuel-injection system and Mallory spark ignition. The engine featured a 5.25x6.50-inch (131.25x162.50-mm) bore and stroke displacing 563 ci (9,222 cc) and rated at 1,050 rpm.

Tested by Nebraska in 1937, the 13,000-pound (5,850-kg) WKO rated 49.26 drawbar and 59.06 belt hp, pulling 11,685 pounds (5,258 kg).

The gasoline-powered WS and WK tractors were tested by Nebraska in 1939. Both tractors featured Allis-Chalmers's four-cylinder, I-head engine rated at 1,050 rpm. The engine of the WS featured a 5.75x6.50-inch (143.75x162.50-mm) bore and stroke displacing 675 ci (11,057 cc) while the WK featured a 5.00x6.50-inch (125x162.50-mm) bore and stroke displacing 510 ci (8,354 cc).

The 20,330-pound (9,149-kg) WS rated 68.86 drawbar and 84.34 belt horsepower. It pulled 17,843 pounds (8,029 kg). The WS featured five forward gears, a Rockford clutch, Zenith 62A12 carburetor, Delco-Remy 12-volt ignition, and Auto-Lite generator and starter.

The 13,340-pound (6,003-kg) WK rated 53.60 drawbar and 62.22 belt horsepower. It pulled 11,785 pounds (5,303 kg), and featured four forward gears, a Fairbanks-Morse FM04-B magneto, and Zenith 62AJ12 carburetor.

1937 Model WK
The "W" prefix denoted the wider-tread version of the Model W. In hilly terrain, the wide track offered extra stability.

1939–1974 HD Series

In 1939, Allis-Chalmers inaugurated its new HD Series of crawlers with the debut of the HD14, soon followed by the HD10 and HD7. All were powered by General Motors two-cycle diesel engines. In 1946, the trio were joined by the HD5 and HD19.

The HD19 was the largest crawler tractor in the world at the time. It weighed 40,000 pounds (18,000 kg), and was ideal for the construction of airfields and roads as well as for use in the logging industry. The machine could excavate twenty-five cubic yards (19 cubic meters) of dirt in ninety seconds—about a quarter of the amount of excavation necessary for the average house.

One of the HD19's key design features was its hydraulic torque converter. The torque converter's development was hastened during World War II when it was needed on the M-4 and M-6 tanks. The torque converter provided greater capacity for work than with other tractors as the liquid-drive principle permitted the engine's power output to be held constantly near maximum.

The HD19's design was the result of the combined experience of the entire tractor organization—dealers, salespeople, operators, and tractor

1937 Model WK
The tractor weighed 13,340 pounds (6,007 kg) and sold new for $2,400. Power was rated at 53.60 drawbar hp.

ABOVE: **1956 Model HD6B**
HD6 crawlers were built over a lengthy period of time, from 1955 to 1974. The HD6B designation of this 1956 model with hydraulic bulldozer blade indicates that it featured a four-roller track. The HD6E model had five rollers and a longer track. The tractor was rated at 50 drawbar hp.

RIGHT: **1956 Model HD6B**
The HD6B crawlers were rated at 50 drawbar hp.

owners. The location and design of the crawler's major assemblies and the parts needing adjustment and maintenance were easily accessible, thereby reducing maintenance and repair costs.

In 1950, Allis-Chalmers replaced the HD7 with the new HD9, the HD13 with the HD15, and the HD19 with the HD20. These crawlers helped create a strong position for Allis-Chalmers in the construction-equipment industry. Allis-Chalmers worked closely with other equipment suppliers to develop full lines of earthmoving, logging, and material-handling equipment for the new crawlers as well.

The Springfield Works was expanded in 1952, marking the twenty-fifth anniversary of Allis-Chalmers's acquisition of Monarch. Allis-Chalmers broke ground for a $15-million expansion, designed to increase production of crawler tractors, motor graders, and repair parts.

At the end of 1953, a torque-converter HD15 crawler was added to the line.

More new crawlers were introduced in 1955. The 31,500-pound (14,175-kg) HD16 crawler was offered with either torque-converter drive or standard transmission. Among its new features was a Wrap-Around radiator guard on which hydraulic rams or lift sheaves could be directly mounted. It also included hydraulic steering and 24-volt direct electric start. The 12,400-pound (5,580-kg) HD6 featured a new Allis-Chalmers four-cylinder, HD344 diesel engine.

Allis-Chalmers Military Crawlers: "Memorialized in Marble"

*I*n this war there are two items of equipment which should be memorialized in marble—the tractor and the jeep," said General Douglas MacArthur, commander in chief of the U.S. Army's Pacific Theater operations in World War II. MacArthur knew firsthand of what he spoke, and his statement lauded companies such as Allis-Chalmers, builders of numerous wartime crawler tractors and tanks.

Allis-Chalmers's crawler needed only slight modifications to be used as an effective tool in World War II. Cooperating with the U.S. Army Ordnance Department, Allis-Chalmers designed medium and heavy high-speed artillery tractors. These units had to be tough enough to haul heavy guns, the gun crew, and the first rounds of ammunition. Two of the company's crawlers became the basis for the famed M-4 and M-6 tractors, which carried Army artillery over rugged terrain to the scene of action.

The M-4 was designed and manufactured at the Springfield Works. The M-6 also was designed in Springfield but was manufactured at the La Porte Works. Small parts and sub-assembly work from the company's facilities in La Crosse and West Allis also went into the units.

"Thanks to Allis-Chalmers workers, these two tank-type tractors are helping the Army get there first with the greatest firing power," reported *WE of Allis-Chalmers.* "They've seen action in Africa and are now carrying the fight to the Axis in Italy, and they'll be there, too, when the Long Toms and the big 240 mm guns begin pounding Berlin."

With their crawler treads, the tractors could plow through trees, mud, and shell holes to get artillery to front lines. *WE of Allis-Chalmers* stated that the 18-ton (16,200-kg) M-4 pulled guns as large as the 155-mm Long Tom. The 38-ton (34,200-kg) M-6 carried the heaviest mobile artillery, the 8-inch and 240-mm guns. Each tractor also was strong enough to carry an artillery crew.

Since the military had used the tractors without many modifications, Allis-Chalmers did not have to redesign the machines for the postwar civilian market. One of the major changes was replacing the army's olive drab paint with the familiar Persian orange.

During the late 1950s and into the 1960s, the Springfield Works and Allis-Chalmers's Construction Machinery Division benefited from the new federal highway bill that earmarked billions of dollars for highway construction over a thirteen-year period. During this time, Allis-Chalmers continued to make advances in construction equipment design and production. Springfield Works was expanded again in 1957, with the construction of additional research and engineering facilities to meet increased demand for machines with greater capacity and power.

In addition to the federal highway bill, the Construction Machinery Division (which included the Springfield Works as well as Allis-Chalmers's plants in Cedar Rapids, Iowa, and Deerfield, Illinois) also benefited from increased dam and industrial construction in the 1960s. The construction field and its allied industries such as cement and aggregates continued to grow. Allis-Chalmers's lines of crawler tractors, motor graders, loaders, and motor scrapers were heavily used by this market. The company also sent numerous crawler tractors to various branches of the armed services during the Vietnam War.

Springfield was expanded yet again in 1969 when Allis-Chalmers built a $1-million worldwide sales and technical services training center next to the production plant there. At the same time, the firm consolidated production plants for more efficient use of facilities. Production from the former Cedar Rapids, Iowa, plants were moved to the Springfield and Deerfield Works.

The Construction Machinery Division faced earnings problems in the late 1960s and early 1970s, however. Allis-Chalmers cut manufacturing and order-handling costs in this sector as much as possible in 1971, which included reducing employment by more than 1,000. A combination of cost-cutting measures and increased industry demand helped turn around the division's earnings performance in 1972 and 1973. In its 1973 annual report, Allis-Chalmers noted that the division responded to sharply increased activity in construction and mining with record shipments.

In 1969, the HD41 crawler debuted, which Allis-Chalmers touted as the world's largest crawler tractor. The 60-ton (54,000-kg) tractor featured 524 hp.

Allis-Chalmers's construction-equipment business attracted the interest of Fiat S.p.A. of Italy. In July 1973, Allis-Chalmers and Fiat announced a joint construction-machinery enterprise. Soon after, the construction-machinery group's sales would no longer be recorded in Allis-Chalmers's accounts. The business had become part of Fiat-Allis.

Farm Commando: Every Machine Has a Job to Do.
—Allis-Chalmers World War II ad, 1940s

CHAPTER 5

Acquiring Advance-Rumely's Tractor and Harvesting Line

MAIN PHOTO: **1920 Advance-Rumely OilPull Type K 12/20**
Advance-Rumely's OilPull was unique in using oil rather than water as a coolant. With its higher boiling point, oil allowed the one- and two-cylinder engines to operate at higher temperatures, making them more efficient when using the low-grade kerosene fuels of the day.

INSET: **1890s Rumely steam traction engine advertisement**
"The Best on Earth," promises this ad for Meinrad Rumely's steam traction engine.

 Soon after it acquired Monarch's crawler line and La Crosse Plow's implements, Allis-Chalmers announced in 1931 that it had bought the venerable Advance-Rumely Thresher Company of La Porte, Indiana. Advance-Rumely was one of the nation's threshing-machine leaders, and its OilPull tractor was legendary. The acquisition provided both a broad line of harvesting equipment and a greatly expanded distribution network. All of this would be essential to Allis-Chalmers as it fought to solidify its position as a leading farm-equipment company in the 1930s and beyond.

Advance-Rumely originated in 1852–1853 as a blacksmith shop in La Porte operated by German immigrant Meinrad Rumely. He began by fashioning farm tools for the immigrants who were moving west. By 1857, the entrepreneur had developed a thresher that could separate 600 bushels of wheat per day.

As his thresher won converts and Rumely's reputation spread, he enlarged his shop. In 1857, Meinrad's brother John joined on and they created the firm M. & J. Rumely. At the same time, Meinrad had been experimenting with horse power for operating threshers; he later became one of the first to adapt steam power to these machines. By 1890, Rumely's threshers were especially popular with farmers with large acreages.

Rumely also developed steam-plowing outfits for farming the heavy soils of the Dakotas and Western Canada. Many of these farmers found that using animals for plowing this tough soil was difficult and expensive. While Rumely's business grew, these first machines had their drawbacks. They needed 1,500 to 3,000 pounds (675–1,350 kg) of coal and 10,000 to 25,000 pounds (4,500–11,250 kg) of water per day. Moreover, the engines weighed from 25,000 to 40,000 pounds (11,250–18,000 kg). Small- and average-sized farms could not justify the huge machines.

The Rumely company thought that gasoline would be too expensive for farmers, so it hired John A. Secor to develop an oil-fueled machine that later became the famous kerosene-burning OilPull tractor. The first OilPull was tested in 1909 and production began in 1910.

The OilPull was developed just as power farming was becoming popular. Several OilPull models were later evaluated in the Nebraska Tests, beginning with the 13-ton (11,700-kg) Model E 30/60 OilPull. With the exception of a Bosch magneto, Rumely used all of its own designs and parts in the OilPull series.

In 1911, the Rumely company bought the Advance Thresher Company of Battle Creek, Michigan, for $5 million. It also acquired Gaar, Scott & Company of Richmond, Indiana, and the famous Northwest Thresher Company of Stillwater, Minnesota. The companies reorganized in 1915, and the Advance-Rumely Thresher Company emerged.

Advance-Rumely broadened its business again in 1923, when it acquired the Aultman & Taylor Company of Mansfield, Ohio, which built tractors and threshers. Aultman & Taylor was a leaders in farm-equipment manufacturing and boasted worldwide sales.

By the time Allis-Chalmers acquired the firm in 1931, Advance-Rumely was one of the world's leading farm-equipment companies. It soon became known as Allis-Chalmers's La Porte Works, and would produce the All-Crop harvester line, Roto-Baler line, One-Man Hay Baler, and many other harvesting-equipment lines. The Indiana facility would also manufacture planters, tillage tools, cultivators, cotton strippers, and manure spreaders.

In 1983, fifty-two years after it had purchased Advance-Rumely, Allis-Chalmers closed down the historic La Porte Works.

Good Equipment Makes a Good Farmer Better!
—Advance-Rumely *OilPull* magazine slogan, 1920s

1910–1912 OILPULL TYPE B 25/45

In 1908, Edward A. Rumely, Meinrad's grandson, hired John Secor to design what became the OilPull tractor. Secor had been experimenting with internal-combustion engines as early as 1885, and his work eventually led to the volume-governing system in modern tractors. Secor replaced an existing Rumely steam engine with a two-cylinder, kerosene-burning engine whose cylinders were mounted side by side and sloped downward from the cab to the front wheels. The tractor was originally called "Kerosene Annie," but was later known as the OilPull.

Secor's OilPull was unique in using oil rather than water as a coolant. With its higher boiling point, oil allowed the one- and two-cylinder engines to operate at higher temperatures, making them more efficient when using the low-grade kerosene fuels of the day.

M. & J. Rumely Company began producing the OilPull Type B in 1910. By the end of the year, the company had built 100 of these tractors rated at 25 drawbar and 45 belt hp. The B carried a two-cylinder engine with 9.50x12.00-inch (237.50x300-mm) bore and stroke. It was rated at 375 rpm.

The B featured the Secor-Higgins carburetor named after Secor and his nephew William H. Higgins, who was the Rumely factory superintendent. The carburetor provided excellent regulation under all loads. The B also featured a low-tension ignition system using a mechanically actuated igniter in each cylinder.

Serial numbers 2101 to 2269 were produced in 1911, and serial numbers 2270 to 2936 were produced in 1912, the last year of production.

1910–1923 OILPULL TYPE E 30/60

Like the B, the OilPull E 30/60 was launched in 1910. It would remain in production until 1923. The popular E featured a two-cylinder, 10.00x12.00-inch (250x300-mm) engine displacing 1,885 ci (30,876 cc) and rated at 375 rpm. The machine included a Bosch low-tension ignition and Rumely's own carburetor.

Nebraska tested the E 30/60 in 1920, but test engineers had problems finding enough ballast to provide an accurate drawbar test for this 13-ton (11,700-kg) monster. The tractor pulled 10,025 pounds (4,511 kg), which corresponded to 49.91 hp. It rated 75.6 belt hp. The E 30/60 had just one forward gear.

1911–1918 OILPULL TYPE F 15/30 AND TYPE F 18/35

The F was a single-cylinder version of the E with its engine rated at 375 rpm. The new tractor had two forward gears and featured a low-tension ignition and mechanical igniter.

In 1918, this tractor was offered as the F 18/35, which more accurately reflected the tractor's performance. The 18/35 offered jump-spark ignition as an option.

1917–1924 OILPULL TYPE H 16/30

The H 16/30 featured a two-cylinder, 7.00x8.50-inch (175x212.50-mm) engine displacing 654.2 ci (10,716 cc) and rated at 530 rpm. This 9,500-pound (4,275-kg) tractor had two forward gears of 2.1 and 3 mph (3.4 and 4.8 kmh), and could be used with the Rumely Ideal 28x44 thresher. It featured a high-tension ignition using a Bosch DU2 magneto.

Tested by Nebraska in 1920, the 16/30 rated 16.68 drawbar and 30.50 belt hp.

1918–1924 OILPULL TYPE G 20/40

The G 20/40 was powered by a two-cylinder engine with 8.00x10.00-inch (150x250-mm) bore and stroke displacing 1,005.3 ci (16,467 cc) and rated at 450 rpm. Tested by Nebraska in 1920, the kerosene-burning tractor recorded slightly over 30 drawbar and 46 brake hp pulling 6,365 pounds (2,864 kg).

The G was introduced in 1918, but production came to a halt in 1924

1920 Advance-Rumely OilPull Type K 12/20

The OilPull Type K 12/20 was built from 1918 to 1924. The venerable OilPull line made its debut in 1910 with the Type B 25/45 and continued through 1930.

along with Rumely's other heavyweight OilPulls. The firm then changed directions, offering smaller OilPulls to meet demand for lighter-weight machines.

1918–1924 OilPull Type K 12/20

A 452.4-ci (7,410-cc), two-cylinder engine with 6.00x8.00-inch (150x200-mm) bore and stroke powered the 6,600-pound (2,970-kg) K 12/20. The engine was rated at 560 rpm. The K had two forward gears of 2.1 and 3.26 mph (3.4 and 5.25 kmh), and came standard with a Secor-Higgins carburetor and Bosch DU20 magneto.

Tested by Nebraska in 1920, this tractor recorded 15 drawbar and 26 belt hp.

OilPull: The Symbol of Power and Dependability.
—Advance-Rumely OilPull ad, 1920s

1924–1928 OilPull Type S 30/60

The largest of the new lightweight series, the S 30/60, featured a two-cylinder, horizontal, valve-in-head engine with 9.00x11.00-inch (225x275-mm) bore and stroke displacing 1,399.5 ci (22,924 cc) and rated at 470 rpm. Tested by Nebraska in 1924, the tractor recorded slightly over 40 drawbar and 60 brake hp.

The S came standard with a Bosch DU4 magneto and Secor-Higgins carburetor. It also featured removable cylinder sleeves.

Advance-Rumely ended production of the S in 1928 after having produced 514 machines.

1924–1927 OilPull Type M 20/35

The 8,750-pound (3,938-kg) M 20/35 was among Rumely's new series of lightweight OilPulls introduced in 1924. The new series featured a lightweight, pressed-steel frame instead of the heavy, structural steel used in Rumely's big tractors.

The M was powered by Rumely's 601.4-ci (9,851-cc), two-cylinder horizontal, valve-in-head engine with a 6.8125x8.25-inch (170.3125x206.25-mm) bore and stroke. The engine was rated at 640 rpm. Also included was a Manzel lubricator, Donaldson air cleaner, American Bosch DU4/2 Ed.22 magneto, and Secor-Higgins carburetor.

Tested by Nebraska in 1925, the M recorded 27.54 drawbar and 43.07 brake hp.

1924–1927 OilPull Type L 15/25

At 6,050 pounds (2,723 kg), the L 15/25 was lighter than the M and was the smallest in the new series of OilPull lightweights. It featured the same engine as the M 20/35, but its bore and stroke measured 5.8125x7.00 inches (145.3125x175 mm), displacing 371.5 ci (6,085 cc) and rated at 755 rpm.

Tested by Nebraska in 1925, the L rated 16.01 drawbar and 25.19 brake hp.

The L came standard with a modified Secor-Higgins carburetor, OilPull cooling system, and Rumely-patented differential lock.

Advance-Rumely produced 4,855 of the L tractors.

1920 Advance-Rumely OilPull Type K 12/20
Advance-Rumely offered sixteen models of OilPulls with one- and two-cylinder engines providing horsepower ratings from the lightweight Type K 12/20 up to the flagship Type Z 40/60 of 1929–1930.

1924–1927 OILPULL TYPE R 25/45

The 11,900-pound (5,355-kg) R 25/45 was powered by a Rumely two-cylinder, horizontal, valve-in-head engine. The engine carried a 7.8125x9.50-inch (195.3125x237.50-mm) bore and stroke displacing 910.8 ci (14,919 cc) and rated at 540 rpm. The R featured three forward gears and an American Bosch magneto.

The 1925 Nebraska test indicated 27.42 drawbar and 50.57 brake hp.

Production of the R was delayed while stock of the G was sold, and just one of the R tractors was built in 1924. The R was produced until 1927, but only 761 tractors were constructed.

1928–1930 OILPULL TYPE W 20/30

The L 15/25 became the W 20/30 in 1928. The engine speed on the W was increased to 850 rpm from the previous 755 rpm. The W's coolant expansion tank also was relocated to the top of the radiator. Other differences between the two tractors were cosmetic.

The W recorded 26.10 drawbar and 35.36 belt hp at Nebraska. Advance-Rumely produced 3,952 of these tractors.

1928–1930 OILPULL TYPE X 25/40

The X 25/40 was a conversion of the M 20/35. The new tractor's crankshaft speed was increased to 725 rpm; otherwise the models were the same. Both models also could be built as special winch tractors.

Tested by Nebraska in 1927, the X recorded 38.66 drawbar and 50.26 belt hp.

Advance-Rumely produced 2,400 of the X tractors from 1928 to 1930.

1929 OILPULL TYPE Y 30/50

The Y 30/50 was converted from the R 25/45. The tractors differed only in engine speed, which was increased from 540 to 635 rpm, and the relocation of the coolant tank from the radiator's back to its front.

Tested by Nebraska in 1927, the Y recorded 47.18 drawbar and 63.32 belt hp.

Just 245 Y tractors were built, and 125 were converted from the R. Five of the Y tractors were in inventory when Allis-Chalmers bought Advance-Rumely in 1931, and were sold at a reduced price.

1929 OILPULL TYPE Z 40/60

The Z 40/60 was a conversion of the S 30/60. Only 215 of these tractors were built.

1934 Allis-Chalmers OilPull catalog

Allis-Chalmers continued to offer the Rumely OilPull line at least through 1934, as shown on this page from Allis's full-line catalog. Allis displayed the three-plow 20/30 OilPull as well as the four-plow 25/40 and monster six-plow 30/50.

1928–1931 DoAll

Advance-Rumely acquired the Toro Motor Cultivator line in 1927 and introduced the DoAll in 1928. The DoAll tractor could be converted into a cultivator, but also was available in nonconvertible form. The DoAll's front wheels and axles could be removed and its rear axle hubs rotated to create a new center of gravity and higher ground clearance. A caster-type rear wheel added stability, and the tractor's steering and control levers were fitted with extensions. The DoAll could be adapted to corn planters, mowers, and other implements.

The DoAll featured a four-cylinder, Waukesha vertical, L-head engine with 3.50x4.50-inch (87.50x112.50-mm) bore and stroke displacing 173.2 ci (2,837 cc) and rated at 1,400 rpm. The tractor had two forward gears and came standard with an Eisemann GV4 magneto, Stromberg MI carburetor, Waukesha governor, and Donaldson-Simplex air cleaner.

In the 1928 Nebraska Test, the DoAll pulled 1,466 pounds (660 kg). Rated power was 16.32 drawbar and 21.61 belt hp.

The DoAll was produced from 1928 to 1931, serial numbers 501 to 3693.

1930–1931 Rumely 6/6A

Rumely started production of its new 6 tractor in 1930, and Allis-Chalmers decided to add the Rumely machine to its catalog following its purchase of the firm in 1931. Known as both the 6 and 6A, the machine was a light, 6,000-pound (2,700-kg) tractor that was still strong enough to pull four 14-inch (35-cm) moldboard plows.

While the 6 was comparable to the Allis-Chalmers Model E in power, the Rumely featured a heavy-duty, six-cylinder, L-head engine with 4.25x4.75-inch (106.25x118.75-mm) bore and stroke displacing 404 ci (6,618 cc). Tested by Nebraska in 1930, it rated 33.57 drawbar and 48.37 belt hp.

Used with its two governed motor speeds, the three-speed transmission gave the operator six forward speeds ranging from 2.5 to 4.75 mph (4–7.6 kmh) and two reverse speeds of 3 to 3.5 mph (4.8–5.6 kmh). The tractor could be ordered with either steel wheels or pneumatic tires.

Allis-Chalmers sold off the remaining stock of Rumely-built 6s and never produced the model itself. Arriving at the dawn of the Great Depression, times were not right for a large, six-cylinder machine. Allis-Chalmers kept the tractor in its catalogs until 1934, proof of how long it took to sell the 802 Rumely 6s that were produced.

1934 Allis-Chalmers Rumely 6A catalog
Allis-Chalmers sold off the last stock of Rumely 6A tractors, as shown on this page from Allis's full-line 1934 catalog.

CHAPTER 6

The Postwar Farm Tractor Boom

<small>Main photo:</small> **1949 Model G**
Basically a "hoe on wheels," Allis-Chalmers's Model G was a truly unique machine. All sorts of attachments were available for the G, including plows, cultivators, and planters as well as a rotary mower.

<small>Inset:</small> **1940s Allis-Chalmers dealer sign**

ALLIS-CHALMERS
TRACTOR DIVISION — MILWAUKEE, U. S. A.

When World War II ended in 1945, it brought an abrupt end to Allis-Chalmers's all-out push to produce war materiel. Suddenly, the company's revenues dropped to $291 million after war contracts totaling about $162 million were canceled in 1945. Now the firm had to focus on returning to a peacetime economy.

The postwar outlook was good for the Allis-Chalmers Tractor Division. The firm did not have to retool or rearrange its factories like other companies in switching to peacetime production. It did, however, share with the industry the woes of material shortages, work stoppages, and supplier strikes. Still, Allis-Chalmers's 1945 annual report stated that the firm had immediately scheduled a return to full production of farm- and construction-machinery lines "in direct bid for a large share of what is generally acknowledged to be the greatest demand for these products in history." The company said it believed that its postwar sales would be limited only by production, and production would be limited only by materials and labor. Despite strikes in seven of its eight plants, Allis-Chalmers offered its most extensive line of agricultural equipment ever in 1946.

Among the many products that the company offered in 1946 was the Model J hydraulically controlled offset disc harrow. Hydraulic control of the disc gangs sped up disking operations and eliminated the physical labor needed for operating a disc harrow.

Throughout 1947, the company reported that farm-equipment demands continued at record levels. At the same time, Allis-Chalmers had another record production year. Along with the one-man baler, Allis-Chalmers began producing a PTO-driven side-delivery tractor rake and tedder as well as the Model 400 tool carrier with several implements for deep-tillage and irrigation farming. Company engineers also had designed a new sweet-corn harvester.

The Tractor Division's new plant in Gadsen, Alabama, started production in early 1948. It was the company's first southern factory, and Allis-Chalmers reported that it enabled the division to produce more farm tractors than ever before, including the unique new Model G.

The Tractor Division sold more than $190 million worth of equipment in 1948, with billings exceeding any previous peacetime year by more than 46 percent. And still demand continued to outstrip supply during the year.

The company reported record peacetime sales again in 1949. Of the company's $352 million in sales, the Tractor Division contributed $207 million in both farm- and construction-machinery sales.

During the 1950s, Allis-Chalmers continued to grow. At the same time, the company enhanced its stance in the farm-equipment business by acquiring other firms, including the purchase of a small plant in Essendine, England, in 1950, and the acquisition of the Gleaner Harvester Corporation of Independence, Missouri, in 1955. The Essendine plant improved the company's farm-equipment sales in Europe. Allis-Chalmers produced the popular All-Crop harvester in Essendine as well as at the La Porte Works. The British-built Model B and other models also helped the company supply customers and support dealers in the United Kingdom and Europe.

After Allis-Chalmers acquired Gleaner Harvester, Gleaner's production facility soon became known as Allis-Chalmers's Independence Works. Together with the All-Crop harvester line, Gleaner aided Allis-Chalmers in grabbing a larger share of the harvester market well into the next decade. The acquisition included Gleaner's popular line of self-propelled harvesters.

In 1950, Allis-Chalmers reported that the Tractor Division had its highest sales figures in the company's history—an amazing $209 million. Included in those sales were crawler tractors, wheel-type farm tractors, harvesting equipment, implements, and materiel for the Korean War.

The war production was a government contract for $180 million worth of military cargo tractors, which were manufactured at the La Porte works. Allis-Chalmers built the M8E2 cargo tractor, one of the U.S. Army's light tank vehicles. It weighed 22 tons (19,800 kg) and could travel at 40 mph (64 kmh). The M8E2 could tow heavy artillery or be used as a bulldozer, wrecker, or hauling unit. At the same time, the division supplied tractor bulldozers, mainly the HD15 to the U.S. Army Corps of Engineers.

The Tractor Division's manufacturing and sales totals were again impressive in 1951. The division recorded volume of more than $265 million, up 27 percent from 1950. Defense production accounted for about 10 percent of Allis-Chalmers's record output. The defense contracts also required that the company expand production capacity, such as adding a 221,000-square-foot (19,890-square-meter) building to the La Porte Works in 1951.

Defense contract sales accounted for more than 16 percent of the company's total sales in 1952. Sales exceeded the 1951 level by more than 11 percent, climbing to $295 million.

The company added to its earth-moving equipment line by acquiring the LaPlant-Choate Manufacturing Company of Cedar Rapids, Iowa, in 1952. This acquisition brought to Allis-Chalmers diesel-powered motor scrapers and motor wagons and tractor-drawn scrapers.

The Tractor Division reported worldwide sales of $280 million in 1953, slightly lower than those of 1952. Allis-Chalmers attributed this to dollar exchange problems, import restrictions by certain countries, and competition from European manufacturers.

The Tractor Division's defense production fell more than $40 million in 1954 so total sales fell to $236 million. However, the WD45 retained its position as the most popular tractor in its power class. Moreover, the company began full-scale production of the new Model 100 self-propelled All-Crop harvester. At its La Crosse Works, the new All-Crop drill went into production; this was a tractor-mounted, precision seeder for use with the WD45 and CA tractors.

Allis-Chalmers in general recorded an all-time sales high of $535 mil-

Pay Dirt Farming!
—Allis-Chalmers ad, 1950s

The Impact of World War II

*A*llis-Chalmers's contributions were invaluable to the winning of World War II, and the war in turn had a dramatic impact on the firm. Moreover, the efforts and sacrifices of Allis-Chalmers's people would make lives immeasurably better for future generations.

Thousands of the company's 36,000 employees saw active duty in the armed services. The numbers varied over the years of the war, but more than 8,000 of the company's employees were in military service as of February 1945.

Between 1940 and April 1944, the firm paid out more than $1 million in benefits to its employees in the military service. Every employee who had worked a year or more with Allis-Chalmers received a month's pay upon entering the service. And starting in 1941, the company also sent as Christmas gifts ten-dollar checks to employees on military leaves of absence.

In addition to monetary reassurance, Allis-Chalmers showed that it remembered its employees in the service by sending them its monthly employee publication, *WE of Allis-Chalmers*. Issues of the magazine featured photographs of employees in the service and updates of where they were and what they were doing. The magazine frequently published excerpts of letters from servicemen and -women. Allis-Chalmers President Walter Geist also regularly sent letters keeping employees apprised of what was happening at the company, and addressing disability benefits and postwar employment.

1944 Allis-Chalmers World War II advertisement
"Let's finish the job!" shouts this ad for Allis's *"Farm Commando"* tractors.

Many of these servicemen and -women saw a variety of some 1,600 Allis-Chalmers products being used in the war effort. These included superchargers, marine-propulsion equipment, crawler tractors and bulldozers, motors and drives, pumps, generators, and more. The company also manufactured direct war materiel, including anti-aircraft-gun mounts, battleship-gun slides, submarine hatches, and other products kept under strict confidence.

Allis-Chalmers reported that it had shipped about $296 million worth of wartime products in 1943. Sales climbed to $381 million in 1944, and the company reported that it had produced three times as much equipment in 1944 as it had the year Pearl Harbor was attacked.

In "A-C Workers Help Sink Subs," *WE of Allis-Chalmers* drove home the point of the company's war role, not only to its employees on active duty, but also to employees who were turning out product back home: "If you work on main or auxiliary D-C generating sets . . . if you help in the construction of main ship propulsion D-C motors . . . if you share in making propulsion or auxiliary electric control equipment . . . if you have a part in making motors for auxiliary drives, pumps for various ship uses, condensers for steam-driven ships, etc, . . . if you play any part in this vast program at Allis-Chalmers—you are helping to sink Nazi subs!"

Two other Allis-Chalmers products that played a huge role in the war were crawler tractors that became the M-4 and M-6 tanks, both designed at the company's Springfield Works.

The war also took men and women away from their farms so Allis-Chalmers's role in farm mechanization took on added significance. *Fortune* magazine in September 1943 wrote that Allis-Chalmers's small combine had "enabled thousands of smaller farmers to mechanize their harvesting. Without it, the demand for farm manpower would have been much greater. It has been called the most useful war tool in the U.S."

Allis-Chalmers recognized that food production was high on the list of items for winning the war, so it did not allow its tractor production lines to be disturbed by military production. In the first few years of the war, however, the U.S. government restricted tractor and farm-machinery production. Output in 1942 was restricted to about 83 percent of 1940 production, and 1943 production was restricted to 23 percent of the 1940 total.

During the war, the company also provided Victory Garden plowing and tilling services. The company's Pittsburgh Works provided free plowing for employees as well as for charitable and public institutions.

However, *WE of Allis-Chalmers* reported that of the six million U.S. farms in 1944, only about one-third were even moderately well equipped. At least two million farms offered excellent potential sales. "The Tractor Division speaks of complete mechanization for a farm to cost about $4,000," it reported.

The Tractor Division was planning ahead to improve its dealer network for the postwar period. The division created a dealer's planning service that studied comments and sketches from dealers wanting to modernize their stores or build new ones. These ideas were matched against "proved requirements" for a successful dealership of that size.

After that, Allis-Chalmers drew floor plans and presented them to dealers. Later, the company showed dealers design ideas using miniature building blocks and small-scale models. As of April 1945, about 150 of 2,700 dealers selling Allis-Chalmers farm equipment were using the service.

By streamlining the dealerships, Allis-Chalmers emphasized repair shops and parts departments. "This means better service to every user who needs to keep his A-C equipment at the vital job of growing food, maintaining roads, building airports or clearing snow from busy streets and highways," the company magazine stated.

The Tractor Division provided sales and service schools to dealers to train them on new and existing equipment. It also beefed up its advertising and sales promotion program.

Both the Tractor Division's $10.5 million La Porte Works expansion, approved in 1945, and stepped-up production at the La Crosse Works also suggested optimism. The in-house

magazine noted that "the postwar plans for La Porte are the outgrowth of the development by Allis-Chalmers engineers of outstanding new farm machines to be priced within the range of the average farmer's pocketbook."

These new machines included the one-person pickup hay baler. The machine was said to enable one person to turn out as many bales as a three- or four-person crew could using a conventional baler.

Another new machine was a lightweight, competitively priced, two-row corn harvester designed for the WC tractor. La Porte Works would provide "a complete line of hay, corn, silage and harvesting equipment in addition to greatly increased production capacity for the Model 60 All-Crop Harvester," reported the magazine.

Allis-Chalmers also laid the groundwork for equipment sales to countries that would need to rebuild their agricultural industries and infrastructures after the war. The company's sales representatives were called to West Allis to discuss postwar business. Export dealers also were sending people from their sales and service organizations to Allis-Chalmers for training.

"It is important to know that the Tractor Division dealer and sales organizations have been carefully maintained throughout the war, so that when war restrictions are lifted our company can quickly resume sales of products to this field," noted *WE of Allis-Chalmers*.

1940s Allis-Chalmers dealer catalog

Allis offered its dealers these "Good Will Builders" in a 1940s dealer catalog.

lion in 1955, and the Tractor Group contributed about 59 percent of this total.

The company also combined its Construction Machinery, Farm Equipment, and Buda Divisions into the Tractor Group in 1955. The Buda, Illinois, facility manufactured material-handling equipment, including lift trucks and industrial towing tractors as well as industrial engines and generator sets.

Allis-Chalmers's sales continued to climb in 1956, reaching a total of $547 million. The newly reorganized Tractor Group accounted for 55 percent of the total, but it was not a good year for farm-equipment sales. The slump was attributed to the combined effect of a long drought and agricultural price adjustments. Allis-Chalmers's new products in 1956 included a front-end delivery manure spreader, Twin-Wheel Drive mower, and Super 100 All-Crop harvester.

This same year, the company established the Allis-Chalmers Credit Corporation, which would help dealers for many years in the farm equipment and other divisions.

In 1957, sales for the company as a whole were $534 million, down $13 million from the record reached in 1956. Farm-machinery sales had picked up, but not enough to offset the decline in construction equipment and heavy industrial equipment.

In 1958, the company's total sales reached $532 million. Whereas the sales figure declined, Allis-Chalmers President R. S. Stevenson said earnings were up 10 percent to nearly $20 million. Farm-equipment sales were substantially up, helped by the new 7½-foot-wide (225-cm) All-Crop harvester, which could harvest more than 100 types of seed crops. The company reported that its four-row cultivator sales rose in 1958, but farmer demand for more capacity stimulated the development of a six-row unit.

1948–1955 MODEL G

With the introduction of the Model G in 1948, Allis-Chalmers pioneered the use of a rear-mounted engine in a tractor. The engine placement provided necessary traction for the machine's two 6x30-inch (15x75-cm) rear tires. The two fronts were 4x12-inches (19x30-cm). The treads on both front and rear tires were adjustable from 36 to 64 inches (90–160 cm).

The G featured two narrow frame members in the front, allowing the operator improved visibility and control while planting and cultivating. This feature was especially popular with farmers who farmed smaller acreages, as well as with vegetable growers and nursery operators. Several different types of implements were made for the G.

The G was powered by a four-cylinder, Continental AN-62, L-head engine. It featured a 2.375x3.50-inch (59.375x87.50-mm) bore and stroke displacing 62 ci (1,016 cc). The engine was rated at 1,800 rpm. The G also featured a Delco-Remy 6-volt electrical system, Donaldson air cleaner, and Marvel-Schebler TSV-13, 0.625-inch (15.6-mm) carburetor. The little, 1,749-pound (787-kg) tractor could travel at speeds of up

1949 Model G
Carrying its one-bottom plow, this 1949 G was ideal for use as a garden tractor or on truck farms. In fact, it's still a highly sought-after tractor for such work.

to 1.6, 2.25, 3.5, and 7 mph (2.5, 3.6, 5.6, and 11 kmh), and a reverse speed of 2 mph (3.2 kmh).

Tested by Nebraska in 1948, the G boasted 9.04 drawbar and 10.33 belt hp and pulled 1,167 pounds (525 kg).

Allis-Chalmers produced 29,970 Model G tractors from 1948 to 1955, serial numbers 6 through 29976. Serial numbers of this unique, highly collectible tractor are stamped on the transmission case top at the rear of the shift lever.

1948–1953 MODEL WD

Along with the Model G, Allis-Chalmers also began production of the Model WD in 1948. This new tractor featured innovations in its design, including power-adjusted rear wheels and an independent PTO. The WD's short wheelbase and compactness made it a popular cultivator.

Prior to the WD's launch, Allis-Chalmers engineers developed the Model D and Model F tractors. These machines had several promising new features, but a lengthy labor strike at Allis-Chalmers forced the firm

ABOVE, TOP: **1950 Model WD**
The WD's short wheelbase and compact stance made it an excellent cultivating tractor. Upon its debut in 1948, the WD featured innovations such as power-adjusted rear wheels and an independent PTO.

ABOVE, BOTTOM: **1950s Model WD advertising poster**
The WD and its implements are shown in this Allis show-room poster.

LEFT: **1950 Model WD**
Many Allis-Chalmers connoisseurs consider the WD to be one of the best tractors made by the company. More than 146,000 WDs similar to this 1950 model were manufactured from 1948 to 1953.

to build a less costly tractor. As a result, the WD was born.

The WD incorporated the best features of the popular Model WC. It was updated, however, with a new power-adjustable rear-wheel system and Traction-Booster hydraulics. Allis-Chalmers's Power-Shift rear wheels allowed the farmer to make quick tread changes without jacking up the tractor. Almost every American tractor manufacturer later included the power-adjustable wheel system on their machines. The new hydraulic system provided weight transfer for rear-mounted implements, including single-hitch-point-mounted implements.

The WD came with an optional adjustable front axle. Tractors were offered with a single- or dual-front-wheel setup. Also unique to the WD was a wet clutch between the PTO shaft and the transmission, providing continuous PTO power independent of ground travel. The main clutch disengaged both drives simultaneously.

The WD used the famous "square" engine first fitted to the WC. The powerful four-cylinder Allis-Chalmers I-head engine had a 4.00x4.00-inch (100x100-mm) bore and stroke displacing 201.1 ci (3,294 cc). It was rated at 1,400 rpm. The WD also featured a Marvel-Schebler TSX-159 1.00-inch (25-mm) carburetor, Fairbanks-Morse FMI 4B3 magneto, and United air cleaner.

The WD evaluated by Nebraska in 1948 was equipped to burn tractor fuel, which was introduced in the 1940s as an alternative to distillate and gasoline. Tractor fuel generally had an octane rating of 42 whereas gasoline ran about 74. The 4,000-pound (1,800-kg) WD recorded 24.31 drawbar and 26.14 brake hp. At the drawbar, it pulled 2,536 pounds (1,141 kg).

The WD was tested again in 1950, fueled this time with gasoline. It rated 30.23 drawbar and 34.63 belt hp and pulled 4,304 pounds (1,937 kg).

1950s Model CA advertising poster
The CA and its implements are shown in this Allis showroom poster.

A wide variety of implements were available for the WD, and many were especially made for it. Along with the standard version, Cane and cotton-picker models were also offered.

In its last year of 1953, the WD cost $1,830. By the time production ended, 146,125 of these popular tractors had been built.

1950–1958 MODEL CA

With the new Model CA of 1950, Allis-Chalmers had a general-purpose wheel-type farm tractor for the two-plow category. It was advertised as matching the all-around superiority of the larger Model WD in its class. This same year, the La Crosse Works began producing a line of new implements for the CA. Engineers designed these implements to be easily and quickly mounted or removed from the tractor.

The CA was more powerful than its predecessor, the Model C. It was equipped with a four-cylinder, Allis-Chalmers CE, vertical, I-head en-

LEFT: **1953 Model CA**
The CA was ideal for farmstead work. It featured power-adjust rear wheels, live PTO, hydraulics, Snap Coupler for mounted attachments, and Traction Booster draft control. Almost 40,000 CAs were sold.

BELOW: **1952 Model CA**
The CA was equipped with a four-cylinder, Allis CE vertical, I-head engine displacing 125 ci (2,048 cc).

1952 Model CA
The CA replaced the Model C and was more powerful than its predecessor to boot. The 2,835-pound (1,276-kg) tractor recorded 22.97 drawbar and 25.96 belt hp at Nebraska.

gine. The engine bore and stroke measured 3.375x3.50 inches (84.375x87.50 mm) displacing 125 ci (2,048 cc). It was rated at 1,650 rpm, compared to the C's 1,500 rpm. The CA featured a Zenith 161AJ7 carburetor, Fairbanks-Morse magneto, and MRI air cleaner. Four forward gears allowed top speeds of 2, 3.50, 4.50, and 11.25 mph (3.2, 5.6, 7, and 18 kmh) and a reverse speed of 3.50 mph (5.6 kmh).

The CA was evaluated by Nebraska in 1950. The 2,835-pound (1,276-kg) tractor recorded 22.97 drawbar and 25.96 belt hp. In second gear, the tractor pulled 2,735 pounds (1,231 kg).

Allis-Chalmers produced 39,499 of these two-plow tractors from 1950 to 1958. Farmers could choose to buy an adjustable front axle or single- or dual-front-wheel types.

1953–1957 Model WD45

Allis-Chalmers expanded the power-to-weight ratio of the WD when it launched the WD45 in 1953. The WD45 was a four-plow tractor powered by a revised four-cylinder Power-Crater engine. Whereas the WD's square engine displaced 201.1 ci (3,294 cc), the WD45 featured a 4.00x4.50-inch (100x112.50-mm) bore and stroke and displacement of 226 ci (3,702 cc). It was rated at 1,400 rpm.

Tested by Nebraska in 1953, the WD45 weighed 8,000 pounds (3,600 kg) and was fueled with gasoline. It rated 37.84 drawbar and 43.21 belt hp. In third gear, the tractor pulled 2,856 pounds (1,285 kg). Allis-Chalmers offered the gas-powered tractor with four forward speeds of 2.50, 3.75, 5, and 11.25 mph (4, 6, 8, and 18 kmh), and a reverse speed of 3.25 mph (5.2 kmh).

The WD45 was tested twice again in 1953, this time fueled by distillate and liquefied-petroleum gas (LPG). In the test using distillate, the WD45 recorded 29.49 drawbar and 33.01 belt hp. In third gear, it pulled 2,204 pounds (992 kg).

In the test with LPG, the WD45 had 38.53 drawbar and 44.13 belt hp. In third gear, it pulled 2,891 pounds (1,301 kg).

Allis-Chalmers offered the WD45 in a diesel version beginning in 1954. This tractor featured an Allis-Chalmers I-head engine with 3.4375x4.125-inch (85.9375x103.125-mm) bore and stroke and 230-ci (3,767-cc) displacement. The engine was rated at 1,625 rpm. The diesel tractor's transmission had ratios that were slightly faster than the gas-fueled counterpart. The WD45 diesel featured forward speeds of 2.50, 4, 5.50, and 12 mph (4, 6.4, 8.8, and 19.2 kmh) and a reverse speed of 3.50 mph (5.6 kmh).

The diesel-fueled version was evaluated by Nebraska in 1955. It weighed 8,035 pounds (3,616 kg) and recorded 39.50 drawbar and 43.29 belt hp. In third gear, it pulled 3,045 pounds (1,370 kg).

1953 Model WD45 advertisement
This ad promises "power to prosper" from Allis's new Power Crater engine.

1956 Model WD45 Diesel
This WD45 is equipped with an Allis-Chalmers fully mounted 8-foot-wide (240-cm) grain drill.

1956 Model WD45
This unrestored WD45 bears paint that's approaching a half-century of usage.

New features were added to the WD45 tractors in 1953, including the Snap Coupler hitch system, allowing farmer to work the hitch from the tractor seat. In 1955, a line of front-mounted, hydraulically operated loaders were released for the WD45 and CA. For the WD45 in 1956, farmers could get factory-installed power steering and Traction Booster, a hydraulic system that provided weight transfer for rear-mounted implements.

Like the WD, the WD45 was available with an optional adjustable front axle. Farmers also could choose single- or dual-front-wheel styles, in addition to Cane and cotton-picker units.

Between 1953 and 1957, Allis-Chalmers produced 83,536 of the WD45 gas and 6,509 diesel models. Serial numbers 146607 through 236958 were located on the rear of the transmission housing.

ABOVE: **1950s Model WD45 brochure**
The full lineup of WD45 versions is displayed in this Allis catalog.

RIGHT: **1956 Model WD45 Diesel**
The engine powering the WD45 Diesel came from the venerable Buda Company of Harvey, Illinois. It displaced 230 ci (3,767 cc) and recorded 39.50 drawbar and 43.29 belt hp at Nebraska.

CHAPTER 7

Allis-Chalmers in Europe

By Bill Huxley

MAIN PHOTO: **1939 Model B**
The Model B was the Allis-Chalmers that British farmers were the most familiar with. Model Bs were common in Great Britain and France in both the English- and American-built versions; this is an early American model.

INSET: **1940s HD7W trio**
A formation of HD7Ws plow hillside land in Wales for potato growing. Most of Allis-Chalmers's crawler range found use on British farms; the M, WM, and HD5 models proved to be the most popular.

ALLIS-CHALMERS
LONDON AND SOUTHAMPTON

Respected British tractor historian Bill Huxley is the author of several other volumes on agricultural history, including most recently *Allis-Chalmers Agricultural Machinery* and *World Harvesters*.

ALLIS-CHALMERS IN GREAT BRITAIN

With the introduction of the Model U in 1929, the Allis-Chalmers tractor department headed by the farsighted, dynamic Harry Merritt found that it now had a tractor of a size and performance more suited to overseas markets than previous models. Allis-Chalmers opened a branch office in 1932 at 728 London Wall, London, England, which handled tractors and other Allis-Chalmers products.

Within a short time, an import base was established at Totton, Southampton, strategically placed to receive incoming goods through the nearby docks that already handled a considerable amount of goods from the United States. Sited in a disused mill, the warehouse initially only handled tractors, but in time also dealt with implements.

One of the earliest Allis-Chalmers dealers was the late Bill Cowlishaw of Methwold, Norfolk. Such was his initiative and drive that upon learning of a rival dealer intending to offer a customer on his patch a different tractor, Cowlishaw promptly assembled the relevant paperwork, mounted his motorcycle, and virtually camped out on the farmer's doorstep. The following morning, a much-surprised farmer was presented with Model U specifications before he could deal with his bacon and eggs. This move brought Cowlishaw's first sale of 1933 and enhanced his company's reputation in the years to follow.

By 1935, Allis-Chalmers was actively promoting its products in Europe, and the Models E 25/40, WC, U, and M and K crawlers were on display at the year's Royal Agricultural Society of England show held at Newcastle Upon Tyne, Northumberland. The "Royal," as it was known, was the premier summer event of this nature and held in a different location each year, making it a first-class venue.

Another early Allis-Chalmers dealer who was probably the most prolific of all was the late John L. C. Flew of Broadbent, Devon, who, having purchased two M crawlers for his lumber business, was then offered the dealership in his area. This turned out to be a brilliant move on the part of Allis-Chalmers. Such was Flew's faith in the product that upon the arrival of the Model B tractor to the United Kingdom market in 1938 that he hauled no less than fourteen of them to a premier west country show. By the end of the event, all had found new owners! No mean feat for a small-time, still relatively new dealer.

In addition to the considerable number of other models and implements that Flew's company sold, it handled more than 1,000 Model B tractors alone. This success was due to Flew's competent and dedicated staff as personified by Ted Pinn. Pinn was stores manager, and was a quiet, competent, and helpful man who was the perfect foil for Flew, who was himself a most charismatic character. Flew remained in busi-

1940 Model U
The larger Model U found a home on some European farms. Farmer Basil White drove this U on a Norfolk estate for many years. Such was his affection for it that upon retirement he promptly bought it and still owns it today.

ness until his death in 1986, and Pinn was still serving well after the usual retirement time.

In the early years, the Models U and M were the big sellers in Great Britain. On the other hand, the WF sold in modest numbers, while the E, A, and K were not big earners. By the end of the 1930s, the B had joined the popular models. Appearing at an inappropriate time in 1939, the RC tried to be all things to everyone but did not set the cash tills ringing. The C achieved modest sales, however.

Following the outbreak of World War II, Allis-Chalmers sought to move operations inland for safe measure, and an unused poorhouse in Abbeydore, Herefordshire, was obtained. Located somewhat off the beaten track, the site did have a rail connection with the Golden Valley Line where off-loading facilities consisted of hand-operated cranes that were a standard feature of many stations at the time.

1935 Model U
Rolling on rubber tires before many of its brethren did, this Model U developed 20.5 drawbar hp—3.3 hp less than if on steel wheels. The U was especially long-lived, being in production for more than two decades, 1929 to 1952.

With the return of peace in 1945, Allis-Chalmers moved back to Totton to a different location and gradually returned to normal activities. The Model B reappeared in 1947, having been axed in 1943 in favor of more pressing imports.

1950–1955 BRITISH MODEL B

Following the war, Allis-Chalmers U.K. started a program of procuring British-produced components. The Midlands-based Rubery-Owen company fabricated sheet-metal goods, Lucas supplied magnetos and electrical items, and numerous other companies joined the list of suppliers. When Bean Industries began production of major castings, an English version of the Model B was built completely in Great Britain.

Serious problems for importers arose in 1949–1950 with the birth of a financial exchange crisis between the U.S. dollar and British pound. In one case, due to the suddenly exacerbated price of U.S. tractors in Great Britain, a batch of forty WFs bound for Totton were impounded at the New York City docks and sent to U.S. dealers as British dealers could not afford them.

Due to the costs of importing machinery, several major U.S. manufacturers established production facilities in Great Britain. Allis-Chalmers's solution was to acquire the Essendine, Lincolnshire, base of Minneapolis-Moline importers Sale-Tilney Ltd., a property ideally located in the midst of arable farming territory. The All-Crop 60 was the principal product from this new factory while the works at Totton were used for other production. With the build-up of product capacity at Essendine, the Totton shop finally closed its doors in 1954.

The British B was the principal tractor built at Essendine in the early 1950s. The tractor underwent various changes over its production life. During development, several diesel engines options were considered as well as a V-twin Turner unit, but the Perkins P3 three-cylinder engine was chosen as the British B's powerplant. The rather basic original hydraulic system was soon superseded by a three-point system affected by simply replacing the drawbar in the forward mounting position for lift-arm mounting. The original top speed of 8½ mph (13.6 kmh) was soon deemed too

1940s British Model B brochure
The B was popular around the globe as it was designed to be a lightweight, small-farm tractor. This brochure from Allis-Chalmers of England notes that "you'll find something this tractor can do for you better, faster, easier, more economically or more profitably than it has ever been done before."

1953 British Model B lineup
An April 1953 sales meeting at Essendine featured the full range of British Bs with implements.

1947 Model B

An ultra-high-clearance vineyard Model B conversion from 1947. Another interesting adaptation of this model was the British Roadless company's half-tracks that were offered in the late 1940s. Owner: J. Willis.

1950s Model B

With its three-point hitch and two-furrow plow, the Model B was a good combination for small farms with light soil. The lack of depth control would be a drawback to sales in the 1950s, how-ever, as implement makers were becom-ing committed to fully mounted ma-chinery.

slow for road work, and when a four-speed transmission was installed, the extra gear offered a top speed of 12 mph (19.2 kmh), which was a more acceptable speed. British B tractors also featured an adjustable front axle and a pan-type seat.

Enterprising dealers also came up with Model B modifications of their own. An ultra-high-clearance version for vegetable cultivation work was built by longtime Essex dealer Ernest H. Doe. A Midlands farmer with an innovative mind created a B conversion to carry irrigation pipe, but with limited visibility and doubtful stability, it was not a sales suc-cess.

By the mid-1950s, the Model B was nearing the end of its production life. Harry Ferguson's TE-20 "Grey Mouse" dominated the small-tractor

1950s D270

A D270 equipped with row-crop wheels in the Netherlands.

end of the market, and the Allis B also had to compete with the smaller International B-250 and Fordson Dexta. As good as the B was, it was never intended to be a universal or mainstream tractor, and it was time for a new model.

1955–1957 D270

The British B was replaced by the D270 in 1955. The D270 was in truth more of an update of the B, with revised sheet metal, improved braking, and a snap-coupler-type hydraulic system with slightly greater output. Matching equipment and implements were available from various suppliers, including the German Rasspe firm and the Wiltshire-based Alvan Blanch company, which supplied Allis-Chalmers with mid-mounted mowers. The D270's most notable option was its hand-operated clutch located on the right-hand axlehousing to give constant PTO operation for baling and other work.

Sales of the D270 in Great Britain were disappointing, however. In France, Peugeot-engined Allis-Chalmers models were faring little better as well. When the D270 was canceled after just two years, the short production span marked it as an interim model.

1957–1961 D272

In October 1957, Allis-Chalmers U.K. launched its new D272 model. The new tractor was an update of the D270, yet still bore traces of the Model B's 1937 beginnings.

The D272 was heavier in appearance than the D270 largely due to its much-revised sheet metal. It carried a more-conventional three-point linkage, and the kerosene power unit now ran at 1,650–1,900 rpm, providing a little more power. The D272 was offered in low (orchard), standard, and high-clearance models to attract a greater range of customers.

The D272 was a good little tractor, but it arrived a little too late. It faced severe competition from other makers as diesel was now becoming the preferred fuel, and most other tractors had a proper hydraulic system to match.

110

1961–1968 ED40

Allis-Chalmers's answer to the situation was announced at a press-release party in a Yorkshire hotel ballroom in November 1960. The new ED40 looked like a savior for the firm. It was based loosely on the U.S.-built D14, two of which were imported for appraisal.

The ED40 featured eight forward and two reverse gears, giving it a top speed of 17 mph (27 kmh). It also boasted "selective weight transfer" hydraulics. These were its positive features, but the ED40 was almost blown out of the water from day one by Allis-Chalmers U.K.'s choice of power unit.

The ED40 was powered by a 2.1-liter (128-ci), 37-bhp Standard-Ricardo 23C diesel. This engine had recently been rejected by Massey-Ferguson in favor of Perkins power owing to its notoriously bad starting characteristics. By July 1963, the trouble had been addressed by installing a glow-plug heater in each cylinder, which greatly improved matters; the revised engine was designated the OE 138 and produced 41 bhp at 2,250 rpm.

What could have become a good tractor was almost destroyed at the same time by replacing the previously satisfactory hydraulics with the dreaded Depthomatic system, which in time caused considerable anguish and expense to owners.

Uneven quality control also beset the ED40. A classic story concerned the Cowlishaw company's new owner, who pointed out a machine defect to an Allis-Chalmers U.K. "expert"; after giving much thought and appraisal to the problem, the dealer suggested an idea that could have gone a long way to solving the problem. The "expert" promptly told him to stick to selling tractors. The net result was that an efficient dealer in a good marketing area promptly lost interest in the ED40.

There was no middle ground in people's reaction to the ED40: Farmers and other users either loved or loathed it depending on their experience. One company that found it ideal for its operations was the British Sugar Corporation, which owned a considerable fleet of some 100 and

ABOVE, TOP: **1950s D272**
A Perkins P3-powered standard model D272 undergoing tests for the well-known engine manufacturer Frank Perkins Company of Peterborough.

ABOVE, BOTTOM: **1950s D272**
A low model D272, possibly inspired by the earlier Ernest H. Doe orchard and high-clearance conversions of the B, necessitated by the vegetable growers in Essex and those in adjacent Kent that produced fruit and hops.

111

1960s ED40

An early ED40 demonstrator in action in East Anglia. Note the early use of 4.00x19 front tires. With a different power unit and greater co-operation from Essendine, companies such as Cowlishaws could have created a much larger market for the ED40.

1960s ED40

A Depthomatic ED40 testing farm machinery at the Mold, North Wales, plant in the hands of John Bumby, longtime employee.

was responsible for having a suitable rollbar produced in the 1970s when legislation demanded its fitting.

Allis-Chalmers made a half-hearted attempt to boost ED40 sales by offering a two-tone paint job for £12-10-0 (£12.50). However, apart from a small band of owners still loyal to the brand, the ED40 was just not being produced or sold in justifiable numbers—a problem no doubt influenced by the fact that Allis's popular four-wheel-drive loaders were being produced at Essendine as well, and the factory could not hope to build both lines of equipment in sufficient numbers.

Following the demise of the ED40, the final new product from Essendine was the 5000 combine, which would prove to be a final throw of the dice for Allis-Chalmers U.K. In 1971, all farm machinery rights and the firm's Mold, North Wales, factory were taken over by Bamfords Farm Machinery Company of Uttoxeter, Staffordshire.

1965 Allis-Chalmers ED40
Similar to Allis's D14, the ED40 was built at Essendine for the British and European market. It featured a 138-ci (2,260-cc) four-cylinder diesel engine and a four-speed transmission with a two-range auxiliary. (Photograph © Andrew Morland)

1960s ED40
An early 37-hp, 2C Standard-powered ED40 with Grays front-end loader. The 4.00x19 front tires were offered with early models; later, 6.00x16 would be standard fitting.

1960s Vendeuvre models

Vendeuvre tractors were on display at a Paris farm show of the early 1960s, with Allis-Chalmers's logo above the stand. These Model R air-cooled machines were soon replaced by the FD range with Perkins power units.

ALLIS-CHALMERS IN FRANCE

Starting in 1915, Éts Tractor of Paris was importing Allis-Chalmers machines into France. With the debut of Model U, Allis-Chalmers's marketing department moved into Europe with a branch office opening in Paris, France, in 1931. Beginning in 1952, British Model Bs were brought to France, followed by the ED40 and American-built D17s.

Unlike the U.K. market, the French market took to the Model G. The G was produced in France from 1951 to 1960, proving it the most popular of Allis-Chalmers machines in the country. Various French versions of the G were offered with designations GR and GRD. Some GRs were even fitted with front-mounted engines.

In 1959, Allis-Chalmers bought the Vendeuvre company of Vendeuvre and Paris, which began production of farm tractors in 1950. Vendeuvre machines were typically powered by one- and two-cylinder air-cooled engines, although three-cylinder models of up to 244 ci (3,997 cc) were also available. Under Allis-Chalmers's ownership, Vendeuvre offered its FD3, FD4, and FD5 range of machines. Vendeuvre tractors were produced in Allis-Chalmers orange up to the closure of the Vendeuvre factory in 1964. After 1968, Allis's plant in Le Havre became the European production center for the growing lift-truck division and small grader production for the construction-machinery division.

ALLIS-CHALMERS IN OTHER EUROPEAN COUNTRIES

Sales in other countries involved import companies such as Lois Reyner in the Netherlands and the Bucher farm machinery company in Switzerland. In Germany, which boasted so many indigenous tractor brands, Allis-Chalmers did not get a strong foothold.

In southern Ireland, Allis-Chalmers products were handled by the old, established McGees of Ardee Company, who imported machinery direct from the United States as well as from Essendine. McGees of Ardee brought over the only WDs to appear in Europe.

THE END OF THE LINE

In hindsight, much of the blame for Allis-Chalmers's lack of long-term success in Europe rests in Milwaukee. Allis-Chalmers U.K. had to do its best to hold onto its market share with one fine tractor of limited ability—the Model B and its revised versions—against competitors who were beginning to offer a range of tractors to suit most applications. Lack of investment and general support created complacency and apathy together with a false sense of security when remembering that a popular line of loaders was being built. The ill-fated Essendine would be mirrored, many years later in the United States, where Allis-Chalmers tried to be all things to every customer. It was a sad, self-inflicted end to a once great company.

1950s Model WF
The Bucher farm machinery manufacturers based in Switzerland handled the A-C tractor up to 1950. This styled WF with a one-bottom, turnover plow had a novel depth wheel system. The belly mower was manufactured by the Rasspe Company.

Chapter 8

The Gateway to the Future: The Stylish D Series

ON THEIR WAY with ALLIS-CHALMERS "D" POWER

to Better Living
Better Farming
More Profit

MAIN PHOTO: **1963 Model D19**
Allis-Chalmers unveiled its new D Series in 1957, offering D Models that would replace all of the preceding tractors over the next couple years. The D19 was Allis's entry into the four-plow tractor market.

INSET: **1950s D Series brochure**
"On Their Way . . . to Better Living, Better Farming, More Profit," pronounces this catalog.

ALLIS-CHALMERS Farming was moving toward larger acreages throughout the 1950s, and so Allis-Chalmers re-designed its tractors, implements, and harvesting machinery for those farmers who needed more versatility and work capacity from their equipment. The January–February 1957 edition of *Allis-Chalmers Scope* put the farm-equipment industry in perspective for the changing times: "With the nation's population growing by almost three million per year, the need for farm products is becoming steadily greater. Recent changes in farming have established modern machines more firmly than ever as a necessary part of profitable farming. Larger farms . . . the need for efficiency . . . the trend toward greater use of tractors in livestock farming—all have increased the need for power farming equipment. The future holds many opportunities for further mechanization and especially for sales of advanced-design machines built for high-efficiency farming."

In 1957, Allis-Chalmers unveiled its dramatic new D Series of tractors. The first two models were the 35-hp, three-plow Model D14 and the 50-hp, four-to-five-plow Model D17. Both had efficient gasoline engines; the D17 was also available as a diesel.

Allis-Chalmers Scope reported in its January–February 1959 edition how Allis-Chalmers gave dealers "ammunition" for positioning the lightweight D17 against competitors. The tractor was compared with two of the competition's tractors. Each tractor was filled with 20 gallons (76 liters) of gasoline and equipped with the same size plows set at the same depth; each tractor plowed in the same soil type until the fuel was gone. The 6,200-pound (2,790-kg) D17, equipped with Traction Booster, plowed 12.1 acres (4.84 hectares). This compared to the 8,760-pound (3,942-kg) tractor that plowed 10.5 acres (4.2 hectares) and the 7,430-pound (3,344-kg) model at 9.1 acres (3.64 hectares).

Allis-Chalmers developed more than 100 tillage implements and planting and seeding machines for the new D Series, including a new line of large-capacity grain and seed drills. It also included a larger, pull-type All-Crop harvester and corn head attachments for two combine lines.

Fueled by the arrival of the revolutionary new D Series, sales for the company were $534 million in 1957, down $13 million from the record reached in 1956. Farm-machinery sales had picked up, but not enough to offset the decline in construction equipment and heavy industrial equipment.

In 1958, the company's total sales reached $532 million. Whereas the sales figure declined, Allis-Chalmers President R. S. Stevenson said earnings were up 10 percent to nearly $20 million. Farm-equipment sales were substantially up, helped by the new 7½-foot-wide (225-cm) All-Crop harvester, which could harvest more than 100 types of seed crops. The company reported that its four-row cultivator sales rose in 1958, but farmer demand for more capacity stimulated the development of a six-row unit.

In 1959, Allis-Chalmers recorded total sales of $539 million. Stevenson said the increase was accomplished despite labor strikes, which shut down the company's major plants for eleven weeks. Despite the work stoppage, Allis-Chalmers introduced two new D Series tractors, the D10 and D12, in 1959. These new tractors were designed to replace the CA and B. The company also offered a complete line of implements for these new machines.

During 1959, Allis-Chalmers demonstrated a device that researchers had already been working on for four years. A fuel cell converted chemical energy in certain common gases into electricity. The fuel cell was mounted in the chassis of a standard farm tractor. The company reported that 15 kilowatts of electrical energy turned a standard Allis-Chalmers 20-hp motor, which drove a tractor pulling a two-bottom plow. In the 1959 annual report, Stevenson said the company planned to continue research and development on this engine. Interestingly, the company noted that the engine had a "theoretical efficiency potential of 80 to 90 percent—approximately double to triple that developed by conventional power sources." The fuel-cell tractor was never produced, but it was an interesting concept.

Allis-Chalmers entered the 1960s riding atop the success of its D Series. The January–February 1960 edition of *Allis-Chalmers Scope* noted how the U.S. population was expected to skyrocket from 179 million in 1960 to 204 million in 1970. Farmers would be challenged to produce enough food and fiber to feed and clothe the population by the decade's end. Allis-Chalmers said it believed the challenge would be met by further mechanization of family farms, greater emphasis on scientific farming methods, and new and improved machinery.

To underscore its understanding of the farmer's food-production challenge, Allis-Chalmers introduced the new Model D15 tractor, Model 72 All-Crop harvester, and 18-foot-header (540-cm) Model C Gleaner and hillside Gleaner combines.

Farm-equipment sales in 1960, however, were down from previous years. Stevenson attributed the sales slump to lower farm prices in 1959 and adverse weather in spring 1960.

In 1961, Allis-Chalmers dealers were invited to an introduction of the company's new farm and utility equipment. More than 300 items were displayed at the Gateway to the Future program. Tractor Group General Manager L. W. Davis cautioned dealers that they would have to earn their share of the future: "During the next ten years, our farmer customers are going to spend $250 billion for equipment, supplies and services. The stakes are bigger; the opportunity is bigger than any of us have ever known before. This is our future."

The 1961 sales improved about 18 percent over 1960. In 1962, retail sales rose more than 25 percent, and sales to dealers were about 20 percent higher than the year previous. At the same time, the Spring 1962 issue of *Scope* reported that U.S. farm income was expected to reach $41 billion in 1962, and net income was expected to hit $13 billion, the highest in ten years.

The Tractor Group's sales reached an all-time high in 1963, 15 percent higher than 1962. More importantly, the Tractor Group contrib-

Better Living, Better Farming, More Profit.
—Allis-Chalmers ad, 1960s

uted 60 percent of the company's total volume. That year, Allis-Chalmers as a whole reported sales of almost $544 million.

The division posted yet another sales increase in 1964. This time, sales were 18 percent higher than the year previous. Davis attributed the increase to substantial gains in tractor and combine sales as well as to growth in the division's industrial and lawn and garden lines.

The Farm Equipment Division set a sales record for the fifth consecutive year in 1965. Allis-Chalmers principals noted that the division's volume had also doubled in five years.

Every one of the company's divisions showed an increase in sales in 1966, and the Farm Equipment Division recorded its sixth consecutive sales record. Sales to the farm, light industrial, and outdoor power equipment markets contributed some $257 million to Allis-Chalmers's sales total of $857 million.

In 1967, sales to these same markets would contribute some $271 million to Allis-Chalmers's sales total of almost $822 million. The company's net income of $5 million, however, fell from the 1966 figure of $26 million.

1950s Model D14 brochure
The "dynamic" D14 was available as a typical tricycle-type tractor and as a high-clearance version, as shown in this catalog. Both gas and LPG versions were offered.

1957–1960 MODEL D14

The Model D14 was introduced to dealers in March 1957 and marked the beginning of a broad and innovative new tractor line. The March–April 1957 edition of *Allis-Chalmers Scope* said the D Series gave Allis-Chalmers "a solid entry in the three-plow field, where 31 percent of all farm tractors are sold."

The D Series incorporated several new features, including the power-adjusted Roll Shift front axle, allowing farmers to adjust front tire tread widths without having to jack up the tractor. The series also featured the Power Director hand clutch, allowing farmers to shift on the go. The Power Director clutch had high and low ranges and was offered in addition to the normal foot clutch. The new clutch also featured a neutral position. Combined with a four-speed constant-mesh transmission, the D14 had eight forward and two reverse speeds.

Features from older models, including Traction Booster and Snap Coupler, were retained. A broad line of ninety implements complemented the D Series. Some of these implements were newly designed, while others were interchangeable with the WD and WD45.

Engineers equipped the three-plow D14 with a four-cylinder, Allis-Chalmers, vertical, I-head engine with 3.50x3.875-inch (87.50x96.875-mm) bore and stroke displacing 149 ci (2,441 cc). It was rated at 1,650 rpm.

The D14 was available as a tricycle type, but high-clearance models were also offered. The standard tractor stood 4.7 feet (141 cm) high, but still had a crop clearance of 25 inches (62.5 cm).

The D14 also featured a constant-speed PTO, enclosed hydraulic system, and adjustable seat, which could be turned over and kept dry when not in use.

The D14 was the first of the D Series to be tested by Nebraska, in

1957. The gas-fueled model provided 30.91 drawbar and 34.08 belt hp.

An LPG-fueled model was tested in 1958. The LPG tractor had a higher compression ratio at 8.5:1 than the regular gas model's 7.5:1. The LPG D14 rated 28.67 drawbar and 31.86 belt hp.

The D14 proved a great success, and from 1957 to 1960, Allis-Chalmers produced more than 22,000 D14 tractors.

1957–1967 MODEL D17

The D17 was in the four-to-five-plow tractor class, replacing Allis-Chalmers's venerable WD and WD45. As proof of its versatility, the D17 was available in gasoline, diesel, or LPG versions with single- and dual-front styles with the Roll-Shift front axle. In addition, a gas D17 cotton version and both cotton and cane diesel D17s were offered as well as an orchard and high-clearance model.

The D17 was equipped with Allis-Chalmers's vertical, four-cylinder, I-head engine with 4.00x4.50-inch (100x112.50-mm) bore and stroke displacing 226 ci (3,702 cc). Like the D14, the D17's engine was rated at 1,650 rpm. However, its compression ratio was 7.25:1 compared to the D14's 7.5:1. Included with the gas model was a Zenith 267-8 1.00-inch (25-mm) carburetor, Delco-Remy ignition, and United air cleaner. The LPG model breathed through an Ensign 1MG1 1.00-inch (25-mm) carburetor.

LEFT: **1966 Model D17 Series IV**
When it made its debut in 1957, the D17 was a truly modern tractor. It was a four-to-five-plow tractor and replaced Allis's long-lived WD and WD45.

RIGHT: **1950s Model D17 brochure**
The "New Concept" D17 was available with either a gas, LPG, or diesel engine.

The D17 diesel was powered by an Allis-Chalmers vertical, I-head engine with six instead of four cylinders. Bore and stroke measured 3.5625x4.375 inches (89x109.375 mm), displacing 262 ci (4,292 cc) but rated at the same 1,650 rpm as the gas engine. Compression was a high 15.7:1, befitting a diesel. Fuel delivery came via a Roosa injector pump.

The D17 included the Power Director hand clutch with eight forward and two reverse speeds. Traction Booster and the Snap Coupler hitch system were also featured.

Both gas and diesel versions of the D17 were tested by Nebraska in 1957. The powerful gas model produced 48.64 drawbar and 52.70 belt hp, while the six-cylinder diesel version had maximum drawbar horsepower of 46.20 and maximum belt horsepower of 51.14.

The LPG version was tested in 1958, providing 46.23 drawbar and 50.79 belt hp.

Both the D14 and D17 were designed mainly for farm use, but Allis-Chalmers also offered them as utility tractors for industrial applications. Several types of implements were available for both D14 and D17 tractors. The company's La Crosse and Oxnard Works provided more than 100 tillage implements and planting and seeding machines for these tractors.

The D17 went through several cosmetic changes but kept the same ratings. The original version—which was retroactively

1959 Model D17 Diesel Series II
The D17's six-cylinder diesel produced 46.20 drawbar and 51.14 belt hp. This tractor was fitted with the Snap Coupler hitch.

known as the Series I—was built from 1957 to 1959 with its basic orange grille; serial numbers ran from 1001 to 23363. A grille with black-painted bars appeared on the Series I from 1959 to 1960; serial numbers were 24001 to 31625.

The D17 Series II arrived in 1960 with the revised Persian orange No. 2 paint and cream-colored grilles and wheels. It remained in production until 1962. Serial numbers were 32001 to 41540.

The D17 Series III debuted in 1962 with serial numbers 42001 through 43358. It was produced from 1963 to 1964 with serial numbers 65001 through 72768.

The D17 Series IV came in 1964 with serial numbers 75001 through

1959 Model D17 Diesel Series II
The D-17 Diesel offered a larger diesel engine than what had been available in the WD45 Diesel tractor—262 ci (4,292 cc) versus the WD45's 230 ci (3,767 cc).

1966 Model D17 Series IV
As proof of its versatility, the D17 was available with single- or dual-front styles. Standard, cotton, cane, orchard, and high-clearance versions were offered.

1966 Model D17 Series IV
The three-point hitch that became available with the Series IV D17 greatly enhanced both its sales appeal and its capabilities.

1966 Model D17 Series IV
The D17 boasted power steering, Roll Shift front axle, Power Adjuster rear wheels, live PTO, three-point hitch, Power Director with eight speeds, and Traction Booster draft control. The D17 Series IV finished production in June 1967.

89213. The D17 was retired in 1967 after a long production life. During its ten-year run, 62,450 D17s in all four series were built.

1959–1968 Models D10 and D12

Two years after Allis-Chalmers introduced the D17, it launched the D10 and D12 tractors. The D10 was designed for one-row cultivation and had a narrower tread. The D12 had a wider front axle and two-row treads for two-row cultivation. Standard and high-clearance versions were available. The high-clearance tractors featured larger rear tires and longer front axle equipment.

Both tractors featured the same four-cylinder Allis-Chalmers 10 vertical L-head engines with 3.375x3.875-inch (84.375x96.875-mm) bore and stroke and 138.7-ci (2,272-cc) displacement. The engines were rated at 1,650 rpm. They featured Zenith 161J7 0.875-inch (21.875-mm) carburetors, Fairbanks-Morse FMJ4B4A magnetos or Delco-Remy 6-volt batteries, and Donaldson air cleaners. Both tractors featured four forward speeds of 2, 3.50, 4.50, and 11.40 mph (3.2, 5.6, 7, and 18.24 kmh) and a reverse speed of 3.50 mph (5.6 kmh).

The D10 and D12 were tested by Nebraska in 1959. The D10 recorded 25.73 drawbar and 28.51 belt hp. The D12 rated 23.56 drawbar and 28.56 belt hp.

In 1961, the D10 and D12's 138-ci (2,272-cc) engine was replaced by a 149-ci (2,441-cc) engine with an increased bore of 3.50 inches (87.50 mm). A 12-volt electrical system was also now used in place of the original 6-volt electrical system on both models. Power was up to 28.78 drawbar and 33.46 belt hp for the D10, 29.43 drawbar and 33.32 belt hp for the D12.

Allis-Chalmers produced the D10 from 1959 to 1968 and the D12 from 1959 to 1967. Series II machines replaced the originals in 1963; Series III models arrived in 1964. The series differences were cosmetic rather than mechanical.

1959 Model D10
The longtime favorite CA was replaced by the D10 in 1959. The D10 was designed for one-row cultivation and had a narrower tread. Standard and high-clearance versions were available.

1961 Model D10
In 1961, the D10 and D12's 138-ci (2,272-cc) engine was replaced by a 149-ci (2,441-cc) engine. Power was now up to 28.78 drawbar and 33.46 belt hp for the D10.

1959 and 1960 Model D10s
Although less than skin deep, there was a major change in Allis tractors between 1959 and 1960. The D-10 on the right was made in 1959 and was painted in what up until then was the standard Persian orange. On the left is a 1960 D-10 that sported the new Persian orange No. 2, also known as Corporate orange.

1960 Model D12
The D10 and D12 came equipped with standard equipment lacked by earlier models: tachometers and three-point live PTOs.

Above: **1963 Model D10 Series II**
In 1963, the D10 and D12 were modified cosmetically and re-released as the Series II.

1964 Model D10 Series III
A further refinement of the D10 and D12 was the Series III, arriving in 1964.

Facing page: **1959 Model D10**
The D10's 138.7-ci (2,272-cc) engines recorded 25.73 drawbar and 28.51 belt hp at Nebraska.

Below: 1964 Model I40
The I40 was an industrial version of the D10 featuring a fixed front axle with a heavy cast assembly and stronger spindle. It also had a steel front end that housed an optional front-mount pump for loader and backhoe applications. The steel front helped protect the radiator. The I40 came equipped with live PTO, live hydraulics, and three-point hitch.

Above: 1960 Model D12
The only major difference between the D10 and D12 tractors was that the D10 could only cultivate one row at time. The D12 had longer rear axles and a different front steering system that allowed the wheel tread to be pushed out far enough to accommodate two rows at a time.

Left: 1964 Model D12 Series III
With the 1961 increase in engine displacement, the D12 recorded 29.43 drawbar and 33.32 belt hp at Nebraska.

Facing page: 1964 Model D12 Series II Hi-Crop
The D12 Hi-Crop version allowed cultivation of row crops at later maturity and taller height. The high-clearance tractors featured larger rear tires and longer front axle equipment.

1960–1968 Model D15

Allis-Chalmers introduced another D Series tractor, the Model D15, in fall 1960. The gas version featured a four-cylinder engine with 3.50x3.875-inch (87.50x96.875-mm) bore and stroke and 149-ci (2,441) displacement. The D15's engine was rated at 2,000 rpm, the highest yet for any Allis-Chalmers tractor.

Engineers equipped the D15 with the Roll-Shift front axle and Power-Shift rear wheels. The tractor featured Power Director and Traction Booster systems. Standard models were available with Roll-Shift and with single- or dual-front wheels. Allis-Chalmers also offered a high-clearance version with Roll-Shift or a single-front wheel.

Tested by Nebraska in 1961, the D15 recorded 35.33 drawbar and 40.00 PTO hp. The D15 LPG rated 33.22 drawbar and 37.44 PTO hp.

A diesel D15 was also evaluated by Nebraska in 1961. This tractor featured an Allis-Chalmers four-cylinder version of the D17 diesel six. The engine had a 3.5625x4.375-inch (89x109.375-mm) bore and stroke displacing 175 ci (2,866 cc). The engine was also rated at 2,000 rpm. The D15 diesel featured 33.32 drawbar and 36.51 PTO hp. The same options available for the gas-powered D15 were available for the diesel.

In 1963, the bore and stroke of the D15's four-cylinder engine was increased to 3.625x3.875 inches (90.625x96.875 mm) to now displace 160 ci (2,621 cc) in Series II guise. Like its predecessor, the engine was rated at 2,000 rpm. A gas-powered D15 Series II tractor was evaluated at Nebraska in 1963, recording 38.33 drawbar and a whopping 46.18 PTO hp. An LPG D15 Series II rated 36.02 drawbar and 43.55 PTO hp.

Allis-Chalmers produced 7,168 D15 tractors from 1960 to 1962 with serial numbers 1001 through 8169. These tractors featured the Persian orange No. 2 paint and cream-colored grilles and wheels.

Between 1963 and 1968, Allis-Chalmers built 12,418 of the D15 Series II tractors with serial numbers 13001 through 25419. The bodies of the Series II tractors were quite similar to the originals, but had different hood decals, lights on the fenders, and black mufflers.

ABOVE, TOP: **1961 Model D15**
When the D15 took the place of the D14 in 1960, it was upgraded to make it a true three-plow tractor.

ABOVE, BOTTOM: **1960s Model D15 Series II brochure**
In 1963, the Series II D15 arrived with a larger engine, now displacing 160 ci (2,621 cc) instead of the D14 and D15 Series I's 149 ci (2,441).

1961–1964 Model D19

The new Model D19 tractor was designed to help Allis-Chalmers serve a growing big-farm, big-tractor market. With its Traction Booster system, the big tractor could pull five-bottom plows.

The D19 featured an Allis-Chalmers six-cylinder engine with 3.625x4.375-inch (90.625x109.375-mm) bore and stroke displacing 262 ci (4,292 cc). The engine was rated at 2,000 rpm and featured an 8.0:1 compression ratio.

The gas version of the D19 was tested by Nebraska in 1962. The

1963 Model D19
The gas D19 produced 63.91 drawbar and 71.54 PTO hp whereas the diesel rated an impressive 62.05 drawbar and 66.92 PTO hp as it was the first American-made diesel tractor to utilize a turbocharger.

powerful tractor recorded 63.91 drawbar and 71.54 PTO hp. It included a Power Director transmission with eight forward gears ranging from 1.9 to 13.9 mph (3–22 kmh) and two reverse gears. Standard equipment included Snap-Coupler hitch and power steering.

The D19 was available with several options, including front- and rear-wheel options, Roll-Shift front axle, and three-point hitch. A high-clearance model was also available.

LPG and diesel versions of the D19 were tested by Nebraska as well. The LPG model produced 58.29 drawbar and 66.19 PTO hp. The six-cylinder LPG engine had a 9.65:1 compression ratio.

The diesel D19 was turbocharged. Allis-Chalmers pioneered use of turbochargers on farm tractors, and the exhaust-driven turbo permitted more power from an engine of a given displacement by driving more air into the fuel mix.

The diesel version of the D19 six-cylinder Allis-Chalmers engine boasted a 14.0:1 compression ratio; following D19 serial number 014419, compression was boosted to 15.0:1. The test recorded 62.05 drawbar and 66.92 PTO hp.

When production ended in 1964, a total of 10,591 D19 tractors had been built.

1963–1969 Model D21

Allis-Chalmers introduced its largest, heaviest, and most powerful tractor yet with the 1963 Model D21.

Engineers equipped the D21 with a six-cylinder Allis-Chalmers diesel engine with a 4.25x5.00-inch (106.25x125-mm) bore and stroke displacing 426 ci (6,978 cc). It had a compression ratio of 16.0:1, and was rated at 2,200 rpm. The engine was the company's first to feature direct-injection diesel, providing easy starting and excellent fuel economy. The transmission had eight forward and two reverse gears.

Tested by Nebraska in 1963, the Model D21 was the only tractor in excess of 100 horsepower to be designed for both drawbar and varied row-crop work: 93.09 drawbar and 103.06 PTO hp were recorded. Allis-Chalmers produced the D21 until 1965 (serial numbers 1001–2129).

When the new Allis-Chalmers One-Ninety XT tractor debuted in 1965, the flagship D21 was suddenly overshadowed by its smaller sibling. To boost power on the D21, Allis-Chalmers engineers added the turbocharger from the D19 diesel engine, creating the D21 Series II tractor.

Tested by Nebraska in 1965, the turbocharger dramatically contributed to the tractor's 116.41 drawbar and 127.75 PTO hp.

Allis-Chalmers produced the D21 Series II tractors from 1965 until 1969, with serial numbers 2201 through 4609.

LEFT: **1964 Model D21**
When the D21 first rolled into the field in 1963, Allis-Chalmers proudly introduced its first tractor to develop more than 100 hp—103.06 PTO hp from 426 ci (6,978 cc)! It was a milestone tractor.

BELOW, LEFT: **1968 Model D21 Series II**
D21 Series II models were introduced in 1965 and ran to 1969. The tractor had an eight-speed transmission, power steering, 540- and 1,000-rpm PTO, three-spool hydraulic valve, three-point hitch, and Traction Booster.

BELOW, RIGHT: **1964 Model D21**
The D21 featured Allis's first adjustable steering wheel, making operating the big tractor for long hours both easier and more pleasant.

CHAPTER 9

The Hundred Series Tractors

MAIN PHOTO: **1970 One-Ninety XT**
The new One Hundred Series was an update of the previous D Series tractors.

INSET: **1960s Allis-Chalmers dealer sign and clock**
Allis introduced a new corporate trademark in 1967. The company created the new trademark after it had set up new divisional responsibilities and reorganized sales and manufacturing facilities. The new trademark would be used on all company products, including this dealer sign and clock.

ALLIS - CHALMERS The trend toward larger farms producing higher yields intensified in the 1960s and 1970s. And the population explosion that Allis-Chalmers had emphasized at the beginning of the 1960s had also come to pass. The average North American farmer was producing enough food to feed forty-three people in 1970, almost three times as much as the previous generation. The burgeoning population was requiring even greater production efficiencies.

Advanced farm equipment, hybrid seed and other crop inputs, and management practices would help farmers produce food more efficiently on larger tracts of land. But those larger tracts of land had to be planted, cultivated, and harvested in the same timely fashion as smaller acreages. The time element coupled with a sharp decline in skilled farm labor put greater pressures on the farmer of the 1970s.

Farmers needed more powerful machinery—particularly higher-horsepower tractors—to get the job done. Allis-Chalmers responded between 1964 and 1981 by introducing its new Hundred Series tractors, which were updates of the company's popular D Series.

Farmers' investments in the faster, more-powerful machines provided a good market for the farm-equipment industry, and Allis-Chalmers for one enjoyed annual sales increases for most of the 1970s.

The Agricultural Equipment Division reported $184 million in sales in 1970, an increase over the $179 million sales figure of 1969. Ag contributed 21 percent of Allis-Chalmers's total sales.

Sales for Allis-Chalmers as a whole and for the Ag Division declined in 1971. The division's sales fell to $174 million. In a letter to shareholders, company President David Scott reported that the Ag Group cut production to reduce high dealer inventories in 1971. This lowered profits, but would clear the way for future improvement, he said.

The company continued to reduce dealer inventories in 1972, so that dealers sold 24 percent more than Allis-Chalmers's production, noted Ag General Manager R. W. Uelner in the 1972 annual report. "Field stocks are now better balanced than at any time since the end of 1967," he added.

The Ag Group recorded $205 million in sales in 1972, representing 21 percent of the company's total sales. Allis-Chalmers offered the broadest line of farm machinery in its existence this year.

The Ag Group recorded another jump in sales in 1973, up to $265 million, contributing 23 percent to the company's total revenues. This was a significant earnings year for Allis-Chalmers in general as President Scott reported that the company's net income was up 87 percent over the previous year.

The 1974 annual report indicated the Ag Group had become part of the Vehicle Groups, which included the Material Handling and Consumer Products Group. Therefore, it is difficult to determine exactly what the Ag Group contributed to the total. Scott reported, however, that the Ag Group had record sales. This year was marked by an energy crisis, inflation, high unemployment, and a rising cost of living. Allis-Chalmers as a whole, however, increased both profits and sales for its fourth straight year.

Allis-Chalmers also reported that the total stock of dealer inventory was at its lowest level in 1974. At that time, the company had a network of more than 1,500 dealers serving customers in North America, Europe, Australia, Southeast Asia, and Latin America.

The company's Vehicles Group enjoyed more record sales and earnings in 1975. Orders for the Gleaner combines and higher-horsepower tractors taxed the capacity of the company's plants and reduced dealer inventories at year-end to low levels. As a result, Allis-Chalmers was making more space available at the West Allis Works to expand production of large tractors, including a new four-wheel drive unit.

The Ag Group enjoyed another good sales year in 1976, despite drought in some areas and weakened farm commodity prices. North American farm income remained at a relatively high level in 1976, and Allis-Chalmers looked to a good farm economy for 1977. But this did not come to pass.

Despite the company's highest ever earnings and sixth consecutive year of earnings improvement, the Ag Group was hurt in 1977. Poorer financial performance was attributed to increased costs and depressed grain prices in the farm economy. The group's profitability also was hurt by strikes at the combine, tractor, implement, and engine plants.

Another key factor affecting profits was an aggressive interest-waiver program that the Ag Group had created to compete with other farm-equipment manufacturers to stimulate retail sales. These waiver programs allowed farmers to delay interest payments on equipment until after they had received cash receipts for their crops. Uelner said this tactic helped Allis-Chalmers maintain a competitive stance.

Yet machinery supply had exceeded demand in 1977, and it was a buyer's market. In this situation, General Manager Harry Lusk indicated that Allis-Chalmers needed to not only keep its current customers, but also to take away customers from competitors.

The Ag Group's 1978 sales and earnings were up marginally over the previous year. The farm economy had improved since 1977, helped by higher commodity prices and an export increase. But the farm-equipment industry still was competitive, reflected in marketing programs offering major price concessions and waivers so farmers could delay interest payments on equipment.

In 1979, the Ag Group recorded its highest sales in history. Its finance expenses, however, increased 30 percent due to higher interest costs.

Allis-Chalmers looked toward the 1980s with caution, noting rising interest rates. In the annual report, however, the firm's spokespeople added that "in spite of short-term uncertainty, the longer-term prospects are favorable because of the basic need for food." The company also indicated that its broad product line and strengthened dealer network would help it face the challenges of the new decade.

Pour on the power for on-time cropping profits.
—Allis-Chalmers ad, 1960s

1964–1973 One-Ninety

The One-Ninety was introduced in 1964 in both gas and diesel versions. Allis-Chalmers reported that the One-Ninety combined slick styling "with efficiency never before offered." The new down-sloping front offered the operator better visibility while the raised, contour seat and adjustable steering wheel provided better operator comfort. The company also called attention to the new tractor's console control: "This console brings the controls of the tractor into one compact area directly under the operator's right hand."

The gas model featured Allis-Chalmers's six-cylinder G2500 engine with a 3.75x4.00-inch (93.75x100-mm) bore and stroke and 265-ci (4,341-cc) displacement. The diesel version was powered by Allis-Chalmers's six-cylinder 2800 engine, featuring a 3.875x4.25-inch (96.875x106.25-mm) bore and stroke displacing 301 ci (4,930 cc). Both engines were rated at 2,200 rpm. The tractor had eight forward gears, ranging from 2.1 to 13.6 mph (3.4–21.76 kmh).

Tested by Nebraska in 1965, the gas version produced 63.10 drawbar and 75.37 PTO hp. In the diesel test, 65.33 drawbar and 77.20 PTO hp were recorded.

The One-Ninety came standard with hydrostatic steering and hydraulically actuated Power Director. Farmers could choose a hydraulically actuated clutch, which permitted independent PTO shaft operation. Single- or dual-front-wheel versions were offered. The Roll-Shift adjustable axle also was available, as was a high-clearance model for special crops. The One-Ninety came standard with three-point hitch or Snap Coupler hitch, as well as Traction Booster.

The gas version of the One-Ninety was built from 1964 through 1968, whereas the diesel model remained in production until 1973.

1965–1970 One-Ninety XT

The One-Ninety gas model also was available as the One-Ninety XT starting in 1965. These tractors were almost identical in outward appearance yet the XT featured an Allis-Chalmers G2800 Power-Crater engine, with more displacement—301 ci (4,930 cc)—than the original G2500 engine.

The One-Ninety XT gas version was built until 1970. A diesel model was offered from 1965 through 1971, and an LPG version was available between 1965 and 1967. By the time One-Ninety XT production ended in 1971, Allis-Chalmers produced more than 22,000 of the tractors.

1970 One-Ninety XT

The One-Ninety XT was a more powerful version of the One-Ninety featuring an Allis G2800 Power Crater engine. The XT displaced 301 ci (4,930 cc) whereas the base model displaced 265 ci (4,341 cc).

1967–1971 ONE-SEVENTY

Allis-Chalmers launched gas and diesel versions of the One-Seventy in 1967. Mechanically, the One-Seventy gas tractor was similar to the D17 Series IV, which it replaced. But its styling was modeled upon the modern-looking One-Ninety. Two-light, flattop fenders distinguished the One-Seventy.

The gas-powered One-Seventy featured a four-cylinder, Allis-Chalmers engine with 4.00x4.50-inch (100x112.50-mm) bore and stroke and 226 ci (3,702 cc) displacement. It was rated at 1,800 rpm. Tested by Nebraska in 1967, it produced 46.93 drawbar and 54.12 PTO hp.

The One-Seventy diesel featured a four-cylinder, Perkins 4.236 engine with 3.875x5.00-inch (96.875x125-mm) bore and stroke displacing 236 ci (3,866 cc). The diesel's engine was also rated at 1,800 rpm. Tested by Nebraska in 1967, it recorded 47.39 drawbar and 54.04 PTO hp.

The One-Seventy came standard with hydrostatic power steering, Power-Director transmission, shift on the go, and continuous 540 PTO. It also was available with a choice of front-end styles and a three-point hitch.

Allis-Chalmers produced the One-Seventy from 1967 until 1971, serial numbers 1005 through 7384.

1967–1973 ONE-EIGHTY

Allis-Chalmers produced a diesel One-Eighty from 1967 to 1973, along with a gas version offered from 1969 to 1970. The One-Eighty diesel featured Allis-Chalmers's six-cylinder 2800 engine with 3.875x4.25-inch (96.875x106.25-mm) bore and stroke displacing 301 ci (4,930 cc). It was rated at 2,000 rpm. Tested by Nebraska in 1967, it produced 55.28 drawbar and 64.01 PTO hp.

The gas version was powered by Allis-Chalmers's G2500 six with a 3.75x4.00-inch (93.75x100-mm) bore and stroke and 265-ci (4,341-cc) displacement. Evaluated by Nebraska in 1969, it featured 56.05 drawbar and 65.16 PTO hp.

The tractor had eight forward gears and included a Power-Director clutch and hydrostatic steering among other standard features. Farmers could choose from single- or dual-front-wheel systems and a Roll-Shift front end. Allis-Chalmers also offered a high-clearance One-Eighty with a single front wheel or Roll-Shift axle.

1969–1971 ONE-SIXTY; 1972–1973 MODEL 160; 1974 MODEL 6040

Allis-Chalmers formed an alliance with Renault of France to manufacture a smaller tractor for both the French and U.S. markets. The Renault-made One-Sixty was launched in 1969 in a diesel version.

This ten-speed tractor was equipped with a Perkins 3.152 three-cylinder engine displacing 152 ci (2,490 cc). The engine was rated at 2,250 rpm. Tested by Nebraska in 1969, the One-Sixty diesel recorded 36.71 drawbar and 40.36 PTO hp.

The One-Sixty became the Model 160 in 1972, when Allis-Chalmers

1969 One-Eighty
The One-Eighty could be ordered with either of two six-cylinder engines: the 301-ci (4,930-cc) diesel or 265-ci (4,341-cc) gas engine. This machine has Roll Shift front axle, Power Adjust rear wheels, hydrostatic power steering, hydraulic Power Director, eight-speed transmission, independent PTO, three-point hitch with Traction Booster, and a two-spool hydraulic valve.

1974 Model 6040
The replacement for the One-Sixty, the 6040, was also built by Renault in France. In 1974, when this 6040 was imported, only 499 of the model made it to the United States.

1971 One-Sixty
The first major tractor that Allis-Chalmers ever imported was the One-Sixty, which was made in France by Renault. This 1971 model is mounted with a scraper blade.

marked the tractor with black decals to match its other large tractors.

Updated again to match the 7000 Series tractors, the Model 160 was renamed the 6040. In the end, Allis-Chalmers produced only about 500 of the 6040 tractors in 1974.

1969–1972 TWO-TWENTY;
1970–1972 TWO-TEN

As a replacement for the flagship D21 Series II, Allis-Chalmers launched its big, 12,000-pound (5,400-kg) Two-Twenty tractor in 1969 and produced this monster until 1972.

The tractor featured a turbocharged, six-cylinder, Allis-Chalmers engine with 4.25x5.00-inch (106.25x125-mm) bore and stroke and 426-ci (6,978-cc) displacement. The engine was rated at 2,200 rpm. In Nebraska's 1969 test, the Two-Twenty diesel produced 117.21 drawbar and 135.95 PTO hp.

The Two-Twenty's rear main housing was much larger and heavier than the D21 Series II. The tractor was equipped with a four-speed transmission with a two-speed range. It included eight forward—ranging from 1.7 to 17.4 mph (2.7–27.8 kmh)—and two reverse gears.

Allis-Chalmers added front wheel assist in 1970, producing just 100 Two-Twenty FWA tractors.

The firm introduced the Two-Ten tractor in 1970, which was similar to its Two-Twenty predecessor, but its PTO power was decreased to 120 hp. Allis-Chalmers needed a tractor with 120 hp to remain competitive. The One-Ninety XT diesel, with 93.64 hp, could not meet that requirement, so engineers used the Two-Twenty as a basis for the new model.

1971 Two-Twenty
The turbocharged six-cylinder engine of the Two-Twenty developed 136 hp from its 426 ci (6,978 cc). It utilized an eight-speed transmission and had a three-spool hydraulic valve.

1970 Two-Twenty FWA
This Two-Twenty FWA featured the front-wheel-assist option, which enhanced both traction and mobility, especially in wet conditions.

Tested in Nebraska in 1971, the diesel produced 104.95 drawbar and 122.40 PTO hp. These tractors were available with protective frames and canopies.

Allis-Chalmers produced 1,471 of the Two-Tens from 1970 to 1972.

1971–1973 MODEL 170

In 1971, the One-Seventy became the Model 170 with an orange grille and black hood decals at serial number 7500. The new 170's hydraulic pump was moved to the front support casting, and its internal steering system was discontinued, eliminating dual-front and single-front wheels. The 170's Roll-Shift front axle had an external steering cylinder.

Allis-Chalmers produced the 170 until 1973, ending with serial number 10300.

1970–1980 MODEL 175

Allis-Chalmers launched its 175 Crop Hustler diesel in 1970 and 175 gas model in 1973.

The diesel featured a four-cylinder, Perkins 4.236 (later changed to a 4.248) engine with 3.875x5.00-inch (96.875x125-mm) bore and stroke and 236-ci (3,866-cc) displacement. The engine was rated at 2,000 rpm. Nebraska tested 54.06 drawbar and 62.47 PTO hp in 1970.

The gas model's four-cylinder, Allis-Chalmers G226 engine featured a 4.00x4.50-inch (100x112.5-mm) bore and stroke displacing 226 ci (3,702 cc). This engine was rated at 1,800 rpm. In Nebraska's 1974 test, it produced 51.80 drawbar and 60.88 PTO hp.

1979 Model 175 Diesel
Built for ten years, the 175 could be ordered with either a four-cylinder 236 ci (3,866 cc) Perkins diesel of 64 hp or an Allis four-cylinder gasoline engine with 226 ci (3,702 cc) and 61 hp. This tractor has hydrostatic power steering, 540-rpm PTO, Power Direct eight-speed transmission, Roll Shift front axle, and Power Adjust rear wheels.

1972 Model 185
The 185 was manufactured for eleven years, from 1970 to 1981. The 185 boasted a high and favorable horsepower-to-weight ratio.

1970–1981 MODEL 185

The 185 Crop Hustler tractor replaced both the One-Eighty and One-Ninety diesels, and was part of an industry trend of using tractor power more efficiently. The 185 featured only a diesel engine since gas tractors had become less popular with farmers.

The 185 was fitted with a six-cylinder, Allis-Chalmers 2800 engine with 3.875x4.25-inch (96.875x106.25-mm) bore and stroke displacing 301 ci (4,930 cc). It was rated at 2,200 rpm. Tested by Nebraska in 1970, it recorded 63.82 drawbar and 74.87 PTO hp. The tractor had eight forward gears, ranging up to 17 mph (27.2 km).

Standard features included the Power Director clutch, Category II three-point hitch, and sway blocks. Farmers could also order special adapters for Category I implements.

The 185 and its 175 counterpart featured Corporate orange (the new Persian orange No. 2) chassis and grille, cream-colored wheels, and black hood decals.

Allis-Chalmers produced 14,961 of the 185 tractors from 1970 to 1981, serial numbers 1001 to 15961.

1972–1975 MODEL 200

Allis-Chalmers's Model 200 tractor came with one of the first factory-made ROPS rollover protection cabs. The 200 was based on the One-

1974 Model 200
The 200 was one those welterweight tractors that are so handy to have around. It could do light- to medium-duty fieldwork, yet also provide the mobility to work around the farmyard and livestock corrals.

Ninety XT, although it featured several upgrades, including a turbocharged diesel engine displacing 301 ci (4,930 cc).

Allis-Chalmers produced 10,126 of these tractors from 1972 to 1975. The Model 200 was replaced by the 7000 Series in 1975.

1972–1976 MODEL 440

With the 440, Allis-Chalmers made a splash in the four-wheel-drive tractor market. Allis-Chalmers purchased this 17,500-pound (7,875-kg) tractor from Steiger Tractor of Fargo, North Dakota. The 440 was based on the Steiger Bearcat.

It boasted a Cummins 555C V8 engine with 4.625x4.125-inch (115.625x103.125-mm) bore and stroke rated at 2,800 rpm. Its compression ratio was 17.0:1. The tractor was not tested by Nebraska, but Allis-Chalmers reported 165 drawbar hp.

The 440 had ten forward and two reverse speeds. It also featured a Dana Spicer clutch, Steiger dropbox, and Franklin axles.

Between 1972 and 1974, Allis-Chalmers offered the 440 with a cream-colored ROPS-certified cab and grille, serial numbers 1001 to 1459. Beginning with serial number 1460 in 1974 and ending with serial number 2010 in 1976, the 440 was available with an orange cab and black grille.

Allis-Chalmers garden tractors
Allis wasn't limited to producing units just for farm fields, as these three garden tractors illustrate. From left, the 1972 16.5-hp 616; 1973 19.5-hp 620; and 1975 19.5-hp 720.

143

CHAPTER 10

The New Family of Tractors

MAIN PHOTO: **1983 4W220**
Allis-Chalmers had come a long way in offering heavy-duty tractors, from its Duplex of the 1920s to the 4W Series that made its auspicious debut in 1982.

INSET: **Allis-Chalmers dealer sign**

1978 7045
The 7045 was powered by a 426-ci (6,978-cc) engine fed through a turbocharger.

Allis-Chalmers engineers began working on what would be called the 7000 Series of tractors in the 1960s. However, the first models resulting from this work were not introduced until 1973, when the 7030 and 7050 made their debuts. These tractors featured all-new styling and were equipped with many new standard features, including all-new powertrains and load-sensitive hydraulic systems, manual and power-shift transmissions, planetary final drives, hydraulic power differential lock, and ROPS cabs.

1973–1981 7000 SERIES

The first models of the 7000 Series—the 7030, 7050, 7040, 7060, 7080, and 7580—stood out from all previous Allis-Chalmers tractors. They featured maroon-colored chassis, engines, and powertrains highlighting the Persian orange No. 2 body and cream-colored wheels and cab roof.

Allis-Chalmers introduced the series with the 7050 in 1973. This 11,000-pound (4,950-kg) tractor featured a 156-PTO-hp diesel engine with twenty forward and four reverse speeds. The new tractor sold for $15,000. The company reported that the 7050 allowed a farmer to increase farm productivity enough to support forty-nine people.

ABOVE: **1978 7080**
Like the other 7000 Series machines, the 7080 was also powered by an Allis six-cylinder 426-ci (6,978-cc) engine. With an intercooler added to its turbocharger, the 7080 upped the power ante to 181 hp. It had a power differential lock, 1,000-rpm PTO, and a comfortable cab with air conditioning and heat.

FACING PAGE: **1978 7045**
The black-chassis 7045 arrived in 1977. It featured multi-disc power brakes, differential lock, planetary final drives, 540- and 1,000-rpm independent PTO, Power-Shift twelve-speed transmission, and a cab with both air-conditioning and heat. This tractor also has the optional heavy-duty front axle.

The maroon-chassis 7000 models included the 7050 and 7030 of 1973–1974; 7040, 7060, and 7080 of 1974–1977; and 7580 of 1976–1977. All were powered by a 426-ci (6,978-cc) engine of 4.25x5.00-inch (106.25x125-mm) bore and stroke with turbochargers; the 7050, 7060, and 7080 also included intercoolers.

In its 1974 Nebraska Test, the big 7080 produced 148.89 drawbar and 181.51 PTO hp. It was bested only by the four-wheel-drive 7580 in 1976 with 186.35 PTO hp.

The 7000 Series was updated with a black chassis in 1977 and included the 7020, 7045, and four-wheel-drive 8550 of 1977–1981; 7060, 7080, and 7580 of 1978–1981; and 7010 of 1979–1981.

1976–1985 5000 SERIES

In the 1970s, Allis-Chalmers formed agreements with several foreign tractor builders to supply models.

To replace the 6040, Allis-Chalmers purchased the 5040 from Uzina Tractorul Brasov (UTB) of Romania. The UTB model was actually a Fiat built under license. The utility machine was offered from 1976 to 1980. It was followed by the Fiat-built 5050 of 1977–1983 and 5045 of 1981.

Toyosha of Japan supplied Allis-Chalmers with four compact

ABOVE, TOP: **978 5020**
A Japanese import manufactured by Toyosha, the 5020 had a 77-ci (1,261-cc) engine that put out 21.8 hp. Toyosha also produced the 5015, 5030, and 5050 Allis tractors.

ABOVE, BOTTOM: **1985 5015**
The 5015 was the smallest of the diesel-powered tractors imported by Allis-Chalmers from Toyosha of Japan.

ABOVE, RIGHT: **1985 6070**
The 6070 was built for only two years. It carried an Allis four-cylinder, 201-ci (3,292-cc), turbocharged engine that gave 70 hp. The transmission had twelve speeds, and the tractor featured independent PTO, planetary final drives, and disc brakes.

tractors: the 5020 of 1977–1985; 5030 of 1978–1985; and 5015 and 6140 of 1982–1985. These tractors were painted orange and featured black chassis and white wheels.

The little 5020 featured a two-cylinder engine with 3.62x3.74-inch (90.50x93.50-mm) bore and stroke displacing 77 ci (1,261 cc) and rated at 2,500 rpm. Tested by Nebraska in 1978, the 2,060-pound (927-kg) diesel produced 17.37 drawbar and 21.79 PTO hp. About 8,500 5020 tractors were produced.

The 5015 had a three-cylinder, Japanese diesel engine displacing 61.3 ci (1,004 cc) and rated at 2,500 rpm. It was rated at 15 PTO hp. While it is unclear how many 5015 tractors were produced, estimates state 3,750. Front-wheel assist was available on the 5015 as well as the 5020.

1980–1985 6000 SERIES

The early 1980s saw the launch of Allis-Chalmers's 6060, 6070, and 6080 tractors. The 6060 and 6080 were replacements for Allis-Chalmers's 175 and 185.

All of the 6000 Series were equipped with a four-cylinder, turbocharged engine with 3.875x4.25-inch (96.875x106.26-mm) bore and stroke displacing 200 ci (3,276 cc). All were turbocharged; the 6080 also boasted an intercooler. As part of Allis-Chalmers's new alliance with Fiat of Italy, the 6000 Series used Fiat's powertrain, front-wheel-assist axle, and three-point hitch.

1984 6060
The 6060 obtained 84 hp from its Allis four-cylinder, 201-ci (3,292-cc) engine. There were eight transmission speeds forward and two speeds reverse.

1984 6060
The 6060 featured disc brakes, differential lock, and a 540-rpm PTO.

1985 6080
Allis offered the 6080 tractor from 1980 to 1985. It carried a four-cylinder, 201-ci (3,292-cc), turbocharged engine that developed 84 hp. This 1985 tractor was offered with differential lock, 540- and 1,000-rpm PTO, twelve-speed transmission, and disc brakes.

149

ABOVE, LEFT: **1982 8010**

Made in the first year of production, this 1982 8010 was powered by an Allis six-cylinder, 301-ci (4,930-cc), turbocharged engine that developed 107.38 hp. The buyer could choose either two-wheel drive (SWD) or mechanical front-wheel drive (MFD) and either Power Shift or Power Director. It came with planetary final drives, 540- and 1,000-rpm PTO, and air conditioning and heat in the cab.

ABOVE, RIGHT: **1982 8030**

The 8030 carried the Allis six-cylinder, 426-ci (6,978-cc), turbocharged engine that put out 133.75 hp. The tractor could be purchased with either SWD or MFD. This particular tractor has the heavy-duty front axle, 540- and 1,000-rpm PTO, and a heated and air-conditioned cab.

The 6060 diesel eight-speed tractor was tested by Nebraska in 1981, rating 50.87 drawbar and 63.83 PTO hp.

A 6080 diesel twelve-speed tractor was also evaluated by Nebraska in 1981. The 6080 produced 70.50 drawbar and 83.66 PTO hp.

The 6070 was introduced in 1984 as an upgrade of the 6060. A 6070 diesel tractor was tested by Nebraska in 1984 and produced 58.35 drawbar and 70.78 PTO hp.

1982–1985 8000 AND 4W SERIES

The 8000 and 4W Series were Allis-Chalmers's last large-tractor lines. With engines and powertrains based on the 7000 Series, the lineups included the 8010, 8030, 8050, 8070, and 4W305 of 1982–1985; and the 4W220 of 1982–1984.

The 8000 Series featured new styling, front-wheel assist, and cabs with heating, air conditioning, and other improvements. Standard features included a twenty-speed Power Director transmission on the 8050 and 8070 models. High-clearance models were available with a twelve-speed Power-Shift transmission.

The 8010 diesel featured a six-cylinder, Allis-Chalmers turbocharged engine with 3.875x4.25-inch (96.875x106.25-mm) bore and stroke displacing 301 ci (4,930 cc). The engine was rated at 2,300 rpm. Nebraska tested an 8010 Power-Shift in 1982 and recorded 91.46 drawbar and 107.38 PTO hp.

The 8030 PS tractor also featured a six-cylinder engine, but this engine had 4.25x5.00-inch (106.25x125-mm) bore and stroke displacing 426 ci (6,978 cc). The engine was rated at 2,500 rpm. In the 1982 Nebraska Test, it recorded 115.22 drawbar and 133.75 PTO hp.

Power was increased again for the 8050 PS. This tractor's six-cylinder, 426-ci (6,978-cc) engine was turbocharged and intercooled and rated at 2,300 rpm. In its 1982 Nebraska Test, it produced 131.44 drawbar and 152.40 PTO hp.

The last 8000 Series Power Shift tractor tested was the diesel 8070,

1985 8050

When this 1985 8050 arrived at the farm, it provided power via a six-cylinder, 426-ci (6,978-cc), 152-hp, turbocharged and intercooled engine. The buyer had a choice of Power Shift or Power Director and either two-wheel drive or MFD. This model had planetary final drives, 540- and 1,000-rpm PTO, and a cab with air conditioning and heat.

1985 8070

Things moved when this 1985 8070's six-cylinder, 426-ci (6,978-cc), 170-hp, turbocharged and intercooled engine started pulling. It was available with either Power Shift or Power Director, and also in the buyer's choice of two-wheel drive or MFD. The cab provided both air conditioning and heat, and the tractor had planetary final drives and 540- and 1,000-rpm PTO.

equipped with a six-cylinder, 426-ci (6,978-cc), turbocharged and intercooled engine rated at 2,400 rpm. Tested by Nebraska in 1982, it fathered 145.36 drawbar and 170.72 PTO hp.

The four-wheel-drive 4W220 and 4W305 tractors were also part of the 8000 Series. The 4W305 featured a six-cylinder, twin-turbo Allis-Chalmers engine. With a 5.25x5.625-inch (131.25x140.625-mm) bore and stroke displacing 731 ci (11,974 cc), it produced 250 PTO hp. A new 4W305 listed at $93,685.

The 4W220 was equipped with an Allis-Chalmers six-cylinder engine with 4.25x5.00-inch (106.25x125-mm) bore and stroke and 426-ci (6,978-cc) displacement. The turbocharged engine was rated at 2,400 rpm. Power was rated at 180 PTO hp.

Both the 4W220 and the 4W305 included Power Director transmissions and enclosed cabs with several comfort features, including soundproofing and a seat with lumbar support.

ABOVE, TOP: **1983 4W220**

Made only from 1982 to 1984, the 4W220 carried Allis's six-cylinder, 426-ci (6,978-cc), twin turbocharged, intercooled engine, which developed 186 PTO hp. Other features were a twenty-speed transmission, 200-gallon (660-liter) fuel tank for long days in the field, and a cab with air conditioning and heat.

ABOVE, BOTTOM: **1985 4W305**

From 1982 to 1984, the 4W305 was the largest Allis tractor. Power came from a six-cylinder, 731-ci (11,974-cc), twin turbocharged engine that developed 305 hp. It also carried a 200-gallon (660-liter) fuel tank, a cab with heating and air conditioning, and worked with a twenty-speed transmission. This particular 1985 model was upgraded with a 400-plus-hp, 855-ci (14,005-cc) Cummins engine.

RIGHT: **1983 4W220 and 1985 4W305**

The Allis-Chalmers "Dynamic Duo!" At left is a 1983 4W220 alongside a 1985 4W305 that's been modified with a larger Cummins 855-ci (14,005-cc) engine of more than 400 hp.

The Selling of the Farm-Equipment Business

The 6000 and 8000 Series were the last true Allis-Chalmers tractors produced before the company was sold in 1985. The sale of the company's Ag Group was due to the failing U.S. farm economy at the beginning of the 1980s.

The decade began with the embargo on U.S. grain exports to the Soviet Union. This created uncertainty in the market, causing grain prices to drop. At the same time, the general economy was marked by high inflation and stagnant growth. To make matters worse, there was a widespread drought and strikes. And the highest interest rates in 180 years made it difficult for U.S. farmers to invest in new equipment. These factors all had an adverse effect on the sales and earnings of Allis-Chalmers's ag line. Interestingly, however, the company's strong product lines, competitive pricing, and financing concessions helped the division gain market share in the 100-hp tractor class and the large-combine business at the time when everything else was in trouble.

Allis-Chalmers continued to add new dealers and support existing dealers. The company's credit corporation was an important sales tool for dealers at this time. "The value of internal credit merchandising was particularly evident during the second quarter of 1980 when many other traditional financing sources, especially rural banks, substantially reduced their commitments to the agricultural area," stated Allis-Chalmers's 1980 annual report.

Allis-Chalmers as a whole suffered a net loss of more than $28 million in 1981 compared to a net income of $47 million the year before. Chairman David Scott reported that while the company worked to reduce ag-equipment inventories and receivables to lower carrying costs, "they contributed substantially to an overall fourth quarter loss of $46.1 million."

Moreover, demand for farm tractors had slipped dramatically. Industry-wide, 1981 tractor sales were down 12 percent from 1980 and down 23 percent from 1979. This could be attributed in part to continued high interest rates. Scott added that the interest waiver program increased almost $10 million, or 38 percent, over 1980; and $21 million, or 147 percent, over 1979.

Allis-Chalmers took several actions to maintain a stable financial condition in 1981, including not producing tractors or combines for much of the fourth quarter. Another included using aggressive selling techniques and competitive terms and discounts to reduce excess stocks. "At year-end, our dealer inventory was reduced to less than 50 percent of annual sales, well below the agricultural equipment industry's average," reported Scott. This also helped Allis-Chalmers gain market share.

The company maintained its North American dealer network during these hard times and also expanded into Africa, Australia, Latin America, Mexico, and the Middle East. At the same time, more dealers were using Allis-Chalmers Credit Corporation financing.

Still, Allis-Chalmers experienced even greater losses in 1982. The company reported a net loss of $207 million and a sales decline of 21 percent

BOTH PHOTOS: **1985 6070**
The end of an era and the last of a great line, this 6070 is the final Allis-Chalmers tractor ever built. "Last Off Line" was written on this 1985 6070's slow moving vehicle sign by the workers on the West Allis assembly line. Carrying serial number 1972, it rolled off the line on the day the plant closed down—December 6, 1985.

compared to 1982. This was attributed mainly to the continued economic slump, particularly in the farm sector. U.S. agriculture was marred by grain surpluses and low prices, continued high production costs, high interest rates, and a drop in exports.

The farm economy took its toll on the farm equipment business in general. Retail tractor sales industry wide fell 25 percent from the previous year. As a result, the industry was discounting equipment on all fronts. Allis-Chalmers stopped tractor production for lengths at a time in 1982 to reduce dealer inventories and equipment carrying costs.

In 1982, the company consolidated its ag equipment and material handling equipment businesses with the financial and insurance service businesses. Allis-Chalmers was working to control expenses and restructure production capacity. It sold its heavy-duty tillage implement business, closed the tractor foundry, reduced the number of employees, and took several other cost-cutting actions.

Allis-Chalmers reported a net loss of $133 million in 1983, an improvement over the year previous. Scott reported that "although it was far from acceptable, the improved performance was achieved in spite of continued depressed markets for all of our major product lines and severe competitive price discounting in many of the markets we serve."

The company continued to control dealer inventories and to match tractor production with retail demand to reduce carrying costs. It also continued some of the other cost-saving measures previously mentioned.

Much of the decline was attributed to the U.S. government's Payment-in-Kind (PIK) program, which significantly reduced acreage nationwide. But a drought, continued high interest rates, and high U.S. dollar exchange rates also contributed to the decline. Retail tractor sales were almost half of what they were in 1979. Adding to the problem was continued discounting.

In 1983, Allis-Chalmers reported that it would pursue some new strategies "to assure a strong, lean base for growth in an emerging market recovery." It would renew its commitment to serving customer needs, maintain product excellence, support dealers, and reduce costs.

To serve customers, the company centralized telemarketing for live prospect referrals to dealers and sales offices. It provided three-year/ 3,000-hour warranties for tractors, guaranteed next-day parts shipment, and flexible financing programs.

Cost reduction also continued. After selling the deep-tillage business and closing the tractor foundry in 1982, Allis-Chalmers next closed the LaPorte, Indiana, implement plant and reduced tractor manufacturing space by 15 percent. The company also reorganized its sales and marketing areas, and out-sourced castings and other tractor components.

Low commodity prices, high interest rates, the strong U.S. dollar, and declining farmland values continued into 1984. As a result, industry unit retail sales declined as much as 50–60 percent in certain product lines, and price discounting intensified.

Sadly, Allis-Chalmers's venerable agricultural-equipment business would soon end. In the 1984 annual report, Scott announced that the company had signed a preliminary agreement on March 28, 1985, allowing West Germany's Klockner-Humboldt-Deutz AG (KHD) to buy Allis-Chalmers's ag business along with Allis-Chalmers Credit Corporation. "The transaction as presently contemplated would include on closing a cash payment from KHD of approximately $107 million and payments to Allis-Chalmers of $23 million from the Credit Corporation," Scott reported.

Tractor sales industry wide continued to slide. Retail tractor sales in 1985 were 58 percent lower than they were in 1979, the last peak-demand period.

Allis-Chalmers had done what it could to cut production costs in the 1980s. But the company reported in the 1985 annual report that the ag market had declined so quickly that Allis-Chalmers had to "accelerate its downsizing efforts, with divestiture as the ultimate result."

Divestiture finally took place on May 24, 1985, and KHD acquired Allis-Chalmers's combine operation, parts-distribution network, and marketing and administrative organization, as well as the Allis-Chalmers Credit Corporation and Financial Corporation. The tractor and diesel engine plants were not included as KHD already had its own plants for those products. Allis-Chalmers produced its last tractor in December 1985.

The Agricultural Equipment Division became Deutz-Allis in 1985. In 1990, Deutz-Allis—as well as Massey-Ferguson, White Tractor, Hesston, and Gleaner—became part of AGCO Corporation of Duluth, Georgia. AGCO continues to distribute the world's largest line of agricultural machinery.

Only one in twenty Americans lived on a farm in 1980 as opposed to 1940 when one in four was a member of a farm family.
—Implement & Tractor, 1980

ALLIS-CHALMERS LIVES ON

While the company is no longer, Allis-Chalmers lives on in countless machine sheds and shops across the country, at auctions, at events such as the annual Allis-Chalmers Spectacular, in collectors' clubs and newsletters, in books and magazines, and on the Internet.

Allis-Chalmers and the spirit of Edward P. Allis, General Otto Falk, Harry Merritt, and others so vital to the company also live on in the memories of the people who worked for this multifaceted company, and who bought and farmed with its farm tractors and implements for the better part of the twentieth century.

Index

About the Authors

Chester "Chet" Peterson Jr. has written numerous other tractor books. He's been involved in farming from his 4-H days, gaining a BS and MS from Kansas State University. Promoted as the youngest associate editor in *Successful Farming* magazine's history, he's worked with a large advertising agency, started and published *Kansas Business News*, and was the publisher of *Simmental Shield*. Chet is now a full-time freelance writer/photographer covering the entire United States and Canada, and specializing in agriculture, aviation, business, and computers. He's a qualified Civil Air Patrol Mission Coordinator and Mission Pilot who can fly his own airplane on assignments, is a certified USA Track & Field Association track official, and has run four marathons. Chet lives in Lindsborg, Kansas.

Lynn Grooms was raised on a purebred hog farm in southeastern Wisconsin, some thirty miles from Allis-Chalmers's home of West Allis. She earned a BA from the University of Wisconsin–Madison in 1981. Grooms has held editorial and public relations positions throughout her career, most notably as editorial director of *Seed World* magazine for nearly ten years. Grooms is now a full-time freelance agricultural writer, and a regular contributor to *Ag Retailer* and *Seed & Crops Digest*. She has co-authored a book published by John Deere Publishing. Her work also has appeared in a several agricultural trade magazines. She lives in Middleton, Wisconsin.

1940s Model B catalog
"Life is Too Short . . . To Farm Without a Tractor," warns this 1940s Allis catalog.

The man with horses works harder and longer to raise each acre of crops.

Because chores for the horses have to be done, his work day begins early.

Before he can start his field-work, there are many extra jobs to be done.

Plodding slowly along, his work is in constant danger of getting behind.

On hot days, he m valuable time to horses . . . work

The man with a slow, heavy tractor spends long, tiresome days in the field.

He hurries through breakfast to get an early start, for he has much to do.

Moving into the field, he hates to think of the endless hours ahead of him.

He is only as fast as his slow power . . . his work chains him to the field.

Bumping along in dust, he is tired b day is half d

The man with a "WC" tractor does his work faster and better, in comfort.

He has no horse chores to do, so his working day need not begin so early.

The tractor is ready to go, and he can start his field-work without delay.

Traveling 2 to 5 times faster than horses, he keeps ahead of his work.

Every hour, his saving money for creasing his p

WHICH DAY *Would*

There is a vast difference between the hopeless drudgery of "just making a living" and the priceless independence of farming to get the most enjoyment out of life. On one hand is the man, with inadequate power, whose work be-

gins before daybreak and ends long after dark. On the other hand is the man with fast, modern power who farms better and makes more money, yet who has plenty of spare time to enjoy his family and his friends. In between is the